ETRURIA:

Jasper, Joists & Jillivers
THE HISTORY OF THE 1986 GARDEN FESTIVAL SITE

written and compiled by

Joan Morley

Dedication

This book is dedicated to, the late Leslie Rogan Hall and his late devoted wife Con, and to all the many thousands who spent their working lives on the site of the 1986 Garden Festival at Etruria, Stoke-on-Trent, including my dear Dad, Bill Lakin, master painter.

Acknowledgements

I am indebted to the following people who encouraged me to write this book, or helped by supplying information:

The late Mr Ernest Warrilow and his wife, the late Mr and Mrs Les Hall, Mr F. Colella, Mr K. Spode, Mr D. Knight, Mrs D. Gough, Mr K. and Mr S. Dunn, Mrs H. Dunn, Mr and Mrs A. Wakefield, Mrs A. Hancock, Miss E. Wardle, the late Mr D. Field, Mr B. Wright, Mr W. Spain, Mr E. Yates, Mr J. Whitehouse, Mrs L. Miller of Wedgwood, Mr F. Foy, Mrs J. Jackson - Keele University tutor, Mrs M. Lakin, Mrs H. Morley, Mrs S. and Miss K. Wood, Mrs H. Baddley, the late Mr L. Green and Mrs Green, Rev. Tony Sutcliffe, Mr Mo Chaudry, and my neighbours Chris and Andrea, who helped me with the problems of technology! and Mr A. Ierston, formerly of Hanley Economic Building Society.

Jasper, Joists & Jillivers:
Jasper for the Wedgwood potters,
Joists for the Shelton Bar steelmakers, and
Jillivers, wallflowers, for the Garden Festival.

The cover is from an original painting by Alf Wakefield. The cost of this cover has been helped towards by Mrs Ruth Trousdale (née Hall), the niece of the late Mr Les Hall, who was so helpful to me in the Shelton Bar section.

CHURNET VALLEY BOOKS
6 Stanley Street, Leek, Staffordshire. ST13 5HG 01538 399033
www.thebookshopleek.co.uk

CONTENTS

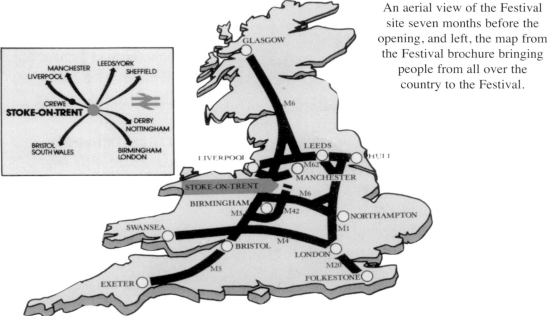

An aerial view of the Festival site seven months before the opening, and left, the map from the Festival brochure bringing people from all over the country to the Festival.

Foreword

If you asked some twenty year olds what they thought of Festival Park, I wonder what the answer would be; a great place for entertainment, good for shopping, eating, meeting friends? Perhaps OK for a city centre walk - on the Woodland Ridge - with girl or boy friends? If you asked them what they knew about the Garden Festival, they would say, "Nothing at all - it was way before my time!" Perhaps "Who's interested in gardening?" Suppose you asked them what they knew about the City's efforts to make the place a greener and more pleasant place to live in? Hopefully they would have noticed something of that, although there is still plenty to grumble about. Some areas of the city are still very ugly and neglected, and the litter is disgusting!

Some schools are now teaching about the great industrial past of the Potteries. This book, I hope, will bring to life some of that amazing history for them in the area where the village of Etruria was established 250 years ago.

Some 25-45 year olds may have a good memory of the Garden Festival of 1986, having found interest and enjoyment there; others will have happy memories of employment on the site. Many will have been thrilled by the tremendous regeneration of the derelict land.

However, I would hazard a guess that the most appreciative people of all will be older still; those who may have spent their working lives on the historic site, or who visited the Festival at every opportunity, finding glorious feasts for eye and mind, and all the thousands of horticultural enthusiasts who worked on or came to see the beautiful gardens. Perhaps the most 'important' visitors of all were the tourists who came to see what the Stoke Festival had to offer. Tourism and service industries are becomeing more important to the prosperity of Stoke-on-Trent, where once mighty manufacturing industries thrived and served the world. Now they have died a death beyond recalling, we must attract all the visitors we can. I hope the book will prove an incentive to new visitors, for the tale it tells is a proud one of hard graft and inspired artistry through the two and a half centuries since Etruria began.

Quote from Alan Godfrey & Trevor Lodge, Old Ordnance Survey Maps, Staffs. Sheet 12,13, 1898:

The Potteries have had a bad press. A postcard of bottle kilns belching smoke has for many years been the most familiar image of the towns; whilst Pevsner's reference to them as "an urban tragedy" summed up the despair of architectural historians. J.B. Priestley had "seen few regions from which nature had been banished more ruthlessly, and banished only in favour of a sort of troglodyte mankind!"

He was even ruder about my own Gateshead, where he caused great offence, but the people of Stoke can scarcely have been happy about his comment that "civilised man ....has not arrived here yet." Orwell and Shaw found it equally hard to come to terms with the place, but earlier writers from Dickens through to Bennett seemed better able to appreciate the strange landscape with its "blazing foundries, its steaming canals, its clay whitened pot-banks, and the marvellous effects of its dust and smoke laden atmosphere" that H.G. Wells described.

Today the smoke has almost gone, and the surviving bottle ovens, glimpsed in the corners of old pottery yards, seem as precious as London's city churches in the shadow of their office blocks. The Potteries are different, and in terms of history they are young, but to the spirited observer they form one of the most fascinating urban landscapes in the realm.

Quote from a newspaper of September 4th, 1990:

Heard on the radio the other night: "The worst place in England must be Stoke-on-Trent.... Many buildings are falling down.... there was supposed to be a garden festival there, but it never got off the ground." For this information we are indebted to an elderly but alert listener at Standon Hall Nursing Home. As an old Fentonian she was furious and was sending her letter to the B.B.C.

Richard Crossman (in 1965 Minister of Housing and Local Government) said:

Here is this huge, ghastly conurbation of five towns - what sense is there in talking about urban renewal here? .... If one spent billions on this ghastly collection of slag heaps, pools of water, old potteries, deserted coal mines, there would be nothing to show for the money..... renewal is an impossibility or alternatively a fantastic waste of money.

(*Diaries of a Cabinet Minister,* Richard Crossman, vol. 1. 1984/6)

Perhaps he forgot that real people lived here. I wonder if he was being challenging or just living up to his name?

Quote from the Bible:

They will rebuild their ruined cities, and live there... they will build gardens...   Amos ch.9, v.14.

Joan Morley 2001

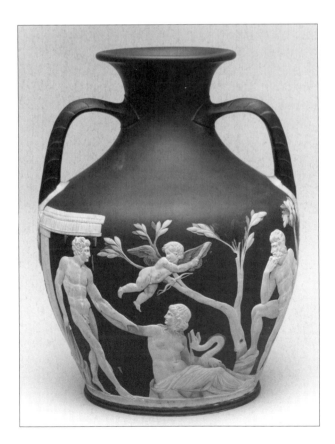

The Portland Vase

PART I

Jasper
THE WEDGWOOD ERA

Wedgwood Creamware

Wedgwood Cauliflower ware 1759-65

A plate from the Empress
Catherine's 'Frog' service.

One

THE BIRTH OF ETRURIA

A quote on Etruria, a village-in-a-city, from a *Chorographical Description of the Flourishing Kingdoms of England, Scotland and Ireland from the Earliest Antiquity, enlarged by the latest discoveries and translated by Richard Gough, 1806:*

ETRURIA

A spot in the parish of Ridgehouse, by a fortunate accident purchased by MR. WEDGWOOD HAS, UNDER THE DIRECTION OF HIS INVENTIVE GENIUS, FURNISHED AN ASTONISHING PROFUSION OF ELEGANT VASES OF EVERY USE AND FORM, AND DESERVED THE NAME ETRURIA, GIVEN TO IT BY ITS INGENIOUS PROPRIETOR.

I found the above in an old book at Newcastle-under-Lyme library, while I was verifying the date of the Robert Morden map of 1722, published fifty years before the village was even thought of! The 'spot' was then an area of windy ground to the west of Hanley, overlooking a long wooded valley which ran towards Longton and separated it from Basford and Newcastle.

THE SITE OF THE FUTURE ETRURIA

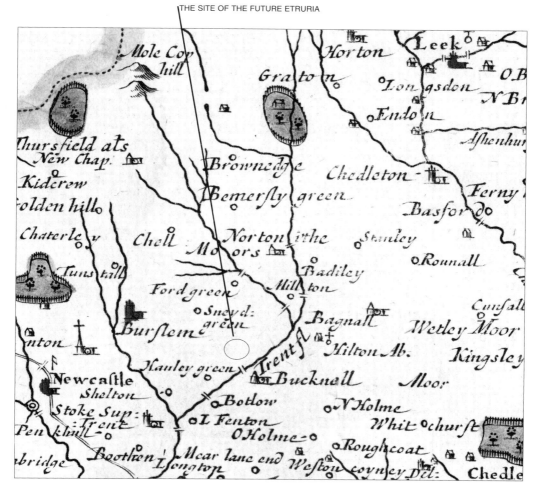

Back in ancient history during the retreat of the Great Ice Age, large deposits of coal and clay formed in this valleys of North Staffordshire, just the materials needed for the making of pottery, although in early days wood was used for the firing. Indeed it is recorded that a settlement of Cistercian monks made pottery and tiles here as early as 1235. Also in the earth were iron and limestone, and small attempts at iron smelting had gone on in the area for 1800 years before our story begins.

Overlooking this valley was the Ridge House Estate occupied by a man, who during the year 1745, when the Scottish Jacobite rebellion reached Leek, had hidden in the valley with his fortune of 60 guineas, and his small son. Other locals followed suit, hiding under the bushes with their children and animals in the grazing land that was to form the site of the Garden Festival more than 250 years later.

Things were set to change when in the middle of the 18th century a young and enthusiastic potter by the name of Josiah Wedgwood came to view the valley in search of a suitable place to build a new potworks along with houses for his workers. He already knew that the proposed route for the Grand Trunk Canal (surveyed in 1755) to join to the Trent and Mersey Canal, lay through this valley, and that this waterway would open up the centre of England to trade throughout Britain and beyond. The mode of transport would eventually cut the cost of getting raw materials to the factories and getting manufactured goods out by an enormous amount. At the time crates of goods were still loaded onto mules or the backs of poor men and women, to be trundled over rough and lonely tracks, to be sold both at local markets and all over the Country.

Wedgwood, an astute businessman, saw immediately the potential of the wooded valley. He knew that the local people were loyal and hardworking, and he was also aware that well

FIGURE 2

Etruria from 'Artes Etruria' - see Ch 12

lodged workers produced better work - for the era he lived in he was a humane man. He decided to buy the estate of 350 acres, owned by a Mrs Ashenhurst, and some extra land to the south - to prevent others trying to build there. The deal was completed in December 1767 for £3,000.

The Ridge House was demolished, and work began on the new factory near to where the banks of the new canal (started in 1766) would run, along with a row of small brick houses for the workers, and a new home for the Wedgwood family lower down the valley, to be called Etruria Hall. The lonely valley became a hive of activity, with 600 men working on the various projects.

The potworks was built to a rectangular pattern with a central tower or cupola and a round house at each end. Sadly all that remains today of this historic building is the Round House nearest the main road, which serves as a unique point of interest for the Sentinel newspaper buildings.

In their new village, the Wedgwood workers, some of them skilled craftsmen, were to have communal bakehouses, an ample water supply nearby and other amenities; they must have felt happy to have secure jobs and homes in an age of grinding poverty and degradation.

Wedgwood pioneered improved roads, in spite of local opposition, people fearing that their country retreats would be overrun with strangers. He had the honour of cutting the first sod of the Grand Trunk Canal on the 2nd July 1766 at Brownhills, near Tunstall - which would run straight in front of his factory and in which he had personally invested £10,000. This canal eventually covered 95 miles of the Midlands and had 75 locks, of which one of the highest was at Etruria. Vital statistics of the canal were: width 29 feet at the top and 16 at the bottom, depth 4 feet.

Until the railway opened in 1846 at least 700 boats passed through the Etruria locks every week! The canal took 11 years to build and Wedgwood was treasurer of the venture for 20 years, taking no wage and paying for embellishments out of his own money. He had part of the canal widened in front of his home to form an ornamental lake, with a small promontory planted with shrubs and trees to form a pleasant view. Local youngsters were allowed to use the pool for swimming, fishing, and skating in winter. Josiah had the surroundings of his home made into beautiful parkland. The potworks too was set in beautiful gardens and was called the 'Factory in a Garden'.

The new village, which a local book has called "a microcosm of the Industrial Revolution", was named Etruria, at the suggestion of Wedgwood's friend and doctor, Erasmus Darwin, after the ancient Etruscan civilisation in Italy from where pottery artifacts were used by Wedgwood as models for his pottery.

Trade from the Potteries was becoming prolific, but the area was held by some in very low repute. Arthur Young, the traveller and writer, wrote: "Let me persuade all travellers to avoid this terrible country!" At the time there were 500 hundred separate potworks employing 7,000 people who worked in appalling conditions, wages being extremely low and bosses cruel and uncaring. The workers at Etruria fared better, for conditions were hygenic and well supervised, and their boss was down to earth and fair-minded.

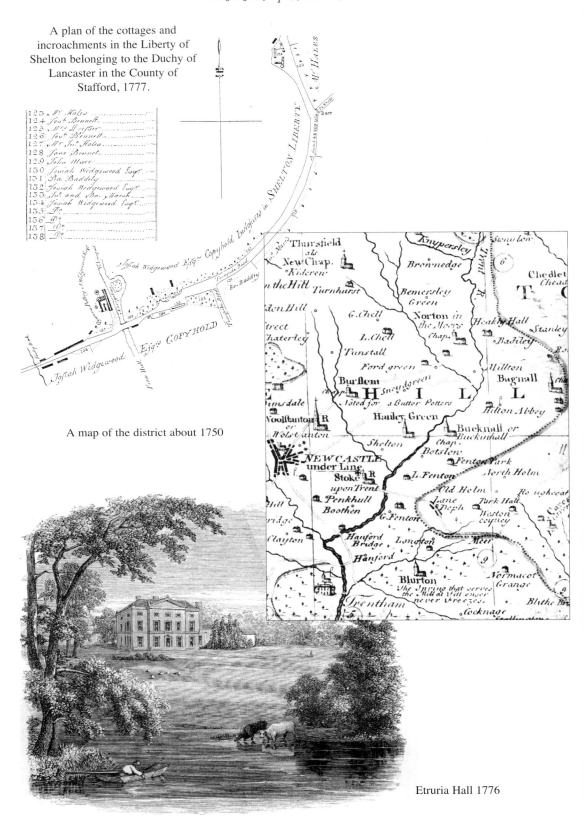

A plan of the cottages and incroachments in the Liberty of Shelton belonging to the Duchy of Lancaster in the County of Stafford, 1777.

A map of the district about 1750

Etruria Hall 1776

Two
THE CANALS OF THE POTTERIES

The canal, road and rail systems in the Midlands, built in the 18th and 19th centuries, were of vital importance to the industrialisation of the area. Without the Trent and Mersey Canal Wedgwood would have been unable to develop into the prodigious industry it became.

The man who planned and built the Trent and Mersey Canal was the British engineer, James Brindley, the 'greatest engineer of the age' (1716-72). Yet he started off his working life as a farm labourer, born on a small farm in Derbyshire and with little or no education. His family later moved to Leek and at 17 he became apprenticed to a millwright in Macclesfield who made mill and associated machinery.

Apparently he was given little help or supervision and was usually blamed for anything that went wrong during his master's absence. However, he must have learned well, for when his master died Brindley moved to Leek, and set up as a millwright himself at the age of 26! He made machinery for flour mills and water driven silk mills, and gained a reputation for reliability and originality. His big chance came when he successfully drained a colliery at Clifton, near to Manchester, by designing and building a tunnel through rock to lead the water away. He came to the attention of the Duke of Bridgewater, who called upon him a year or two later, in 1759, to construct a canal leading from the Duke's collieries at Worsley to Manchester. It was a marvellous achievement which took two years to complete, and included the carrying of the canal over the River Irwell by an aqueduct, regarded by many at the time as an impossible and foolish task! It must have been a sight in those days to see barges crossing high over the river.

He constructed a wind-mill at Burslem for grinding calcined flint for the potworks of Josiah Wedgwood's uncle John. Then he was approached about the construction of the canal to link the Trent and Mersey Rivers, which was to be called the Grand Trunk Canal. In 1765 an association had been formed and a Bill was passed in Parliament for the building of the new waterway. Brindley was appointed Surveyor General at an annual salary of £200 and began to work on the great project. It took 11 years to complete, and when finished in 1777 the canal linked the two rivers across the breadth of the Midlands and was an engineering triumph. At its highest point it went through a tunnel 2 kilometres long, the Harecastle Tunnel.

Brindley went on to construct canals in the larger area of the Midlands, in all some 365 miles of them! But sadly Brindley himself did not live to see the fruition of his scheme of the Grand Trunk canal system, dying from diabetes and perhaps self neglect at 56 years of age.

Canal builders were referred to as navigators, and he had the popular title of "Brindley the Navigator": This is where the word 'navvy' originated meaning labourer, and especially applied at first to canal, then rail, and later road workers.

Here is a whimsical note about the canal building which recognises some of Brindley's character, from a letter of Wedgwood's, to his friend Bentley, about some graceful curves he had wanted building into the canal channel in front of Etruria Hall. He is referring to the clerk of the works... *"I could not prevail upon that vandal to give me one line of grace - he must go the nearest and best way or Mr. Brindley would go mad!"*

It is amazing to realise that James Brindley had difficulty with reading and writing, and many of his problems and endeavours were solved without the aid of writings or drawings. He would go to bed and ponder long and deeply to solve his problems and work out his schemes. His principal planning tool was his surveyor's level and this can be seen now at the Brindley Mill at Leek, along with one of his notebooks, and other possessions. There is a memorial statue to the great man erected appropriately at the point where the Trent and Mersey and Caldon Canals meet in Etruria (and there is another in Birmingham).

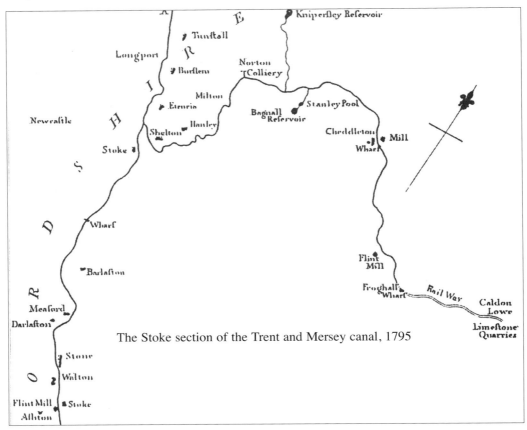

The Stoke section of the Trent and Mersey canal, 1795

The Caldon Canal went from the Trent and Mersey at Etruria to Froghall, and was opened in 1788. It is 17 miles in length, and was a vital key to the expansion of the North Staffordshire industrial towns, which eventually became today's Stoke-on-Trent. It was used to carry limestone from Caldon Low, iron ore from Froghall, coal from Norton Green and flint from Consall Forge and Cheddleton, to the industries requiring these raw materials. Pottery and paper were also transported round the area by canal. Wedgwood gave some interesting details about the canal boats in a letter to Sir William Hamilton:

"The canal boats are 70 ft. long and 7ft. in breadth, tonnage is 1¹/₂d. per mile for goods in general. Dung, manure and materials for roads are free, and time is only ¹/₂d. per ton per mile."

The Caldon Canal was later extended to Uttoxeter, but this extension was soon superceded by the new railway. The canal was little used in the present century and fell into disrepair until the City Council decided to reclaim it. A £100,000 scheme restored it to a navigable state, and now the whole canal system is much enjoyed by cruising holiday makers, as well as walkers and cyclists.

Close to Brindley's statue at Etruria is the Etruria Industrial Museum, the restored Jesse Shirley Bone and Flint Mill of the 19th century. It was built in 1857 to grind materials for the pottery and agricultural industries and is the only remaining steam driven pottery mill in the Country. It continued in production until 1972 and its machinery and processes are virtually in tact. The 'Princess' steam engine is in steam regularly once a month, run by enthusiastic museum staff and a loyal band of volunteers. This is a highly recommended place to visit!

A quote from Wedgwood's letters concerning James Brindley is appropriate here, for it shows how highly the potter esteemed the engineer:

● **The statue of James Brindley, made in clay at the Henry Doulton school of sculpture at Fenton.**

When completed, the bronze James Brindley will be transported from London back to the Potteries in the historic steam narrow boat President, using the canal system by Brindley after leaving the Thames.

Guy Barks is hoping that the statue will eventually be placed on a site alongside the Caldon Canal at a little wharf where pottery workers set out as emigrants to America in the 1840s.

This little-known spot is a short distance from the junction of the Caldon Canal and the Trent and Mersey at Shelton, where a canalside museum is being created at Shirley's bone mill and an adjoining blacksmith's shop.

This work should all be completed in time for the unveiling of the statue, when Brindley's genius will at last be publicly recognised in the Potteries.

From the Evening Sentinel

March 2nd. 1767

"I am afraid he will do too much, & leave us before his vast designs are executed; he is incessantly harrassed on every side, that he hath no rest, either for his mind, or Body, & will not be prevailed upon to take proper care of his health."

28th Sept. 1772 (after Brindley's death)

"Mr. Brindley had an excellent constitution, but his mind, too ardently intent upon the execution of the works it had plann'd, wore down a body at the age of 55 which originally promis"d to have lasted a Century & might give him the pleasing expectation of living to see those great works completed for which Millions yet unborn will revere and bless his memory...... Do I need to tell you that he bore his last illness, with that fortitude & strength of mind which characterised all his actions?"

Etruria early 20th century

A plate from Empress Catherine's "Frog" service showing Etruria Hall

Three
JOSIAH WEDGWOOD I

Josiah Wedgwood was the youngest of the 12 children born to Thomas and Mary Wedgwood, of an old, respected family of potters of Burslem. He was born in early July, 1730, and baptised on the 12th of that month at the church near their home. He was a bright, intelligent child whose hobbies included geology and nature study.

When his father died in 1739 he had to leave school and go to work at the Churchyard Pottery Works, now taken over by his brother Thomas. He was nine and was pitched into the potworks with no further schooling, but he worked hard and became an excellent thrower, continuing his studies in his spare time. Unfortunately a short while later he contracted smallpox which left him weak and ill, affecting his right leg in particular from which he had much pain (later, in 1768, he had to have it amputated, without anaesthetic, which had not been invented then).

He continued to work and to study however, and at the age of 14 (November 1744) became apprenticed to his brother for 7 years. The leg pain forced him to leave the thrower's bench and this proved a blessing in disguise, for he went on to learn all the other branches of the potter's art. At 24 he entered a five year partnership with Thomas Whieldon of Fenton, the most noted potter of the time, from whom he learnt a great deal, experimenting with him in *"the body of the wares"* and developing new colours, glazes and forms.

In 1759 Wedgwood became his own master when he leased the Ivy House Works at Burslem for £10 a year. He was 28. His first notable achievement was the invention of a brilliant green glaze, good for models of fruit and vegetables, the famous 'Cauliflower' ware dating from this time. He also produced delicate articles of small ornamental ware, such as snuff boxes and knife handles. He trained a small dedicated staff of workers who respected his skill and artistry.

Another move was made in 1762 to the Brick House Works, later called the Bell Works, since he called his employees to work by a bell instead of the usual horn, reckoning it better for wakening them up. Here he produced the cream ware that became famous later as Queen's Ware, *"a new species of earthenware, of a firm and durable body, covered with a rich and brilliant glaze, and bearing such vicissitudes of cold and heat without injury..... accompanied also with the advantages of being manufactured with ease and expedition, was sold cheap, and consequently came quickly into general estimation and use."* From 1765 the gold was fired permanently into the ware instead of being fixed by oil size.

Wedgwood employed ceramic printers in Liverpool and Leeds to decorate the ware, transfer-printing being cheaper and quicker than hand painting. It was said that he put fine earthenware within the reach of all but the very poor. There were very many of the latter at that time of course, almost beneath the notice of great manufacturers, who did all the menial tasks for a pittance.

The greatest order for Queen's Ware came from the Empress Catherine of Russia, who required a combined dinner and dessert set for 50 people, numbering a staggering 952 pieces! This order took almost a year to complete, and was decorated with authentic English scenes of palaces, mansions, cottages, parks, gardens, forests, cathedrals and even a canal lock, taken

Etruria in 1794 with the windmill behind.

from all over the Country, including local views of places like Keele Hall, Trentham and Newcastle. The scenes, many taken from books of fine engravings, numbered 1,234 (another source puts the number at 1282!), and were hand painted by leading painters and ceramic artists of the day, in a deep mulberry colour, each piece having on it the emblem of a frog from the crest of the Empress (her palace was near to marshy ground). The art work alone made the ware priceless in value. When the work was completed in 1774 payment received was just over £2,700, whilst Wedgwood's expenses had been at least £2,612, so the financial rewards were small - however the publicity gained more than compensated for that.

By 1766, when Wedgwood had begun to receive huge orders, he knew he needed larger premises and he began to look around for a suitable site. So it was that Etruria came into existence. Here the concept of division of labour came into its own. It was at Etruria, during the 1770s, that he developed his famous Jasper, perfected in 1774 after thousands of experiments - vitreous stoneware in blue, green, lilac, yellow and black. Sometimes two colours were used in the same piece, being decorated with white classical reliefs or portraits, (the original moulds for which are still preserved and the reliefs are still applied by hand. My husband remembers visiting the Etruria factory as a young schoolboy and being given a piece of one of these while watching them being applied by a friend's dad.)

Wedgwood prized Jasper above all his other achievements. Some was used in plaques for decorating fireplaces, furniture and clocks at Etruria Hall and other great mansions. Wedgwood was pleased, after a cool initial reception to the ware, by the enthusiasm of his friend Sir William Bagot of Blithfield, who showed him a room full of marvellous paintings and Jasper decorations. When Wedgwood noticed and lamented a little chip at the edge of a tablet, Sir William said that, on the contrary, it was a fine thing - a happy accident, for it showed the merit of the fine texture, coloured all the way through and not merely on top!

Wedgwood's crowning achievement in this body was his famous replica of the Barberini or Portland vase (see pp. 6 & 20) an example of glass cameo cutting dating back to about 25AD. He produced this in 1789 after years of experiments, spending the large sum of £600 before he was satisfied. The vase is of dark blue overlaid with white, into which are cut classical figures in relief. Sir Joshua Reynolds declared Wedgwood's to be a true and worthy Jasper copy of the original, and one of the world's outstanding achievements.

Josiah loved art in all its forms and engaged leading artists and sculptors of the day to assist him. He was highly sensitive to what was topical, and swift to react to current events. This can be seen in the fact that when news of the French Revolution (which began on July 14th 1789) reached England, he had in production portrait medallions of the people involved by the end of the month! He was an ardent anti-slave campaigner and he produced thousands of small medallions modelled for him by William Hackwood, showing a slave kneeling in chains with the inscription; *"Am I not a Man and a Brother?"* These medallions were given free to anti-slavery supporters and a large parcel of them was sent to Benjamin Franklin in the newly independent United States. The

The Slave Medallion 1787

latter thanked Wedgwood, saying that they were as effective as the best written pamphlet. The little medallions were mounted as hatpins and jewellery, or used as buttons, and became very popular both at home and in America. Clarkson, a prominent member of the Anti-Slavery Committee, commented that for once *"fashion was supporting a useful cause, that of justice, humanity and freedom!"*

Wedgwood's greatest partnership was with Thomas Bentley, a Liverpool merchant, whom he met in 1762, a man of outstanding gifts - linguist, classicist, traveller and diplomat, a charming and cultured man who made an outstanding contribution to Wedgwood's success. The partnership lasted from 1769 until Bentley's untimely death in 1780. Bentley was a great marketeer and managed the showrooms and decorating studio at Chelsea in London, where some of the ware was decorated until Wedgwood had the artists brought to work at Etruria. The showrooms became fashionable meeting places for the rich and famous, excellent for both advertisement and trade.

Bentley never actually lived at Etruria, although a house had been built for him along with the rest of the village to the south of the Hall and called Bank House (it was demolished in 1819).

Thomas Bentley

An invitation to view the Portland Vase in the London showroom.

From a Victorian magazine depicting scenes of industry at Wedgwood's Etruria.

Fine Wedgwood ware.

Josiah and his family lived there for a year until their own home was completed. Bentley further helped Wedgwood, by his knowledge of Parliamentary procedures, in land schemes and the breaking of monopolies of clay suppliers, for example. From 1770 no more local clay was used in the making of table ware, china clay coming from Devon and Cornwall, but Josiah also used earth and clays from all over the world.

Josiah Wedgwood was not a professional chemist but his knowledge of chemistry and physics was far ahead of that of any other potter of his time. He invented an ingenious new instrument for measuring very high temperatures called the 'pyrometer', and published and read papers on this, and on the chemistry of clays, to the Royal Society, as a result of which he was elected a Fellow. He became President of the New Chamber of Manufacturers of Great Britain in 1785. He supported many good causes including free schooling in Burslem, road improvements and free trade in Ireland.

In 1790 Josiah partially retired from some of his active duties and took longer holidays, for his health was deteriorating. After a short illness he died on 3rd January 1795, at the age of 64. He was buried in Stoke churchyard and a memorial was erected to his memory inside the church. It was modelled by John Flaxman Junior and on it were written these words:

Sacred to the Memory of
JOSIAH WEDGWOOD, F.R.S. and S.A.
Of Etruria in this county.
Born, August 1730.   Died January 3rd. 1795.

"Who converted a rude and inconsiderable
Manufactory into an elegant Art and
An important part of National Commerce."

[Note the slight mistake in regard to the great man's birth......no one knows why]

A bronze statue of Wedgwood was erected outside Stoke Station 68 years after his death. William Burton, a modern ceramic expert, wrote of Wedgwood:

His influence was so powerful, and his personality so dominating that all other English potters worked on the principles he had laid down, and thus a fresh impetus and a new direction was given to the pottery of England and of the civilised world. He is the only potter of whom it may be truly said that the whole of the subsequent course of pottery manufacture has been influenced by his individuality, skill and taste!

Memorial plaque to Josiah Wedgwood
in Stoke parish church

Further fulsome praise comes from the compilers (Finer and Savage) of his letters to his much loved colleague Bentley, who say: *"His remarkable alliance between beauty and productivity was the touchstone of Wedgwood's success."* and *"He organised his factory with the efficiency of a business consultant."*

Four
THE FAMILY MAN AND FRIEND

Josiah and Sarah Wedgwood from a painting by George Stubbs.

Josiah Wedgwood was a great family man and friend to many. He married his third cousin Sarah on January 25th 1764 and she made him an excellent and loving wife. He valued her opinion in all matters, saying, *"I speak from experience in female taste, without which I should have made a poor figure amongst my potts, not one of which of any consequence is finished without the approbation of my Sally."*

They had seven children of whom six survived, some becoming famous in their own right in different spheres. When the family settled in Etruria Hall Josiah compiled a timetable for the children's education for what he called the 'Etruscan School' and engaged various tutors for them. He shared his hobbies with them, including gardening and riding in the lovely country lanes near their home. They were a very happy family, given to entertaining.

Josiah's concern for his family is shown in the interest he took in his scholarly nephew Thomas Byerley, a lively teenager, saying, *"I do not know what we shall do with him, to keep him out of mischief, & put him into a way of being of some use in the World!"* Thomas was sent to America at the age of 20 as a private tutor. When he returned in 1775 Josiah took him on as general assistant for translating and writing in French, teaching the children and travelling for the firm. He went with Josiah's son, Josiah II, on an extended tour of France, Germany and Holland to show the Portland Vase. After Thomas Bentley's death, Byerley took over management of the London showrooms.

Bentley was a much loved visitor to Etruria Hall and his death in 1780 was a great blow to all the family. Whenever the two friends had been apart they had corresponded daily, and

Wedgwood's letters make fascinating reading. His closest friends shared with him his love of experiment, enquiry and invention, and also his love of art. They included Joseph Wright of Derby, who gave him a painting of Dovedale as a 'thank you' to 'a gracious Patron and Encourager of Living Artists'. Josiah responded with the gift of a table service in green shell edge.

Another friend was Joseph Whitehurst, geologist and scientific instrument maker (1713-88). He sent earths and clays to Wedgwood at Etruria for analysis, and designed a kiln for him, built in 1769. He also supplied the Etruria works' clocks for the various departments - a useful addition to the smooth running of the factory!

Thomas Byerley - a great worker for Wedgwood's.

These friends of Wedgwood belonged to a group called the 'Lunar Society' which met monthly in Birmingham at the full moon - so that the members could return home safely in its light - and occasionally he would accompany them home. Founder members included Matthew Boulton (canals and steam engines) and Erasmus Darwin, anti-slave campaigner and doctor, whose son, Robert Waring Darwin, married Wedgwood's eldest daughter, Susannah. The marriage produced a son who was to become one of the most famous and controversial men of the 19th century, Charles Darwin, author of *The Origin of Species*. Members of the group were sometimes referred to as 'the lunatics', an amusing epithet for such clever individuals.

It is interesting to note here that the connection between the two illustrious families of Wedgwoods and Darwin lasted for well over a hundred years, since Charles Darwin married Emma Wedgwood, daughter of Josiah II, who lived at Maer Hall, a beautiful country residence. The marriage took place at Maer church in 1839 and was a long and happy one.

It is easy to forget that for a large part of his working life Wedgwood had only one leg, for this handicap seems not to have prevented him from living life to the full. We read from his letters that following the amputation he used a peg leg for a year, but after that a jointed one was made and maintained for him by a local joiner. Frequent repairs were necessary, as illustrated by the following bill:

To a new bolt and repairing the leg   £ 0. 10sh. 6d.
To repairing the leg and thigh and making a new foot   £ 1. 11sh. 6d.

In a letter to his friend Dr Darwin, dated June 27th 1788, Wedgwood wrote: *"An ingenious joiner in this neighbourhood is making me a new one, which I believe is nearly finished; he has made one or two before and had the care of the old one for many years, and it has received so many repairs from him that it is now become like the sailor's knife which had so many blades and so many hasps."*

Obviously Josiah Wedgwood was never a man to let personal pain or discomfort stand in the way of his art or his enjoyment of life, nor his ongoing concern for other people in general. His story is a lesson in the true art of living!

Five

THE ETRURIA WORKS

The new potworks at Etruria covered seven acres of ground and was built in two distinct sections - the White Bank Square for making cream, later Queen's, ware (useful ware), and the Ornamental Works Square, where the Jasper and Basalt (decorative) ware was made.

Wedgwood organised his factory so that each workshop was separate with its own entrance and stairway, so the workers had to go out of doors to pass from one workshop to another. Presumably this arrangement was allied to the fact that he trained his workers to a specific skill, a division of labour which he was one of the first industrialists to practise. Probably it also made the overseeing of each section more thorough, while dissuading employees from wasting time visiting other workshops, especially in cold weather! But in truth the workers were treated in a humane manner and were able to move about freely: the harsh and tyrranical rule which held sway in other potworks did not apply here. A friendly and hard working atmosphere prevailed and generations of the same families worked for the firm - you had to be recommended in order to get a job there!

Workers standing outside the Etruria works early 1900s.

The fashion for tea drinking in the 1750s led to a great demand for crockery - sorry, 'equipages', this being the favoured word in the pottery industry. Wedgwood was quick to respond; he developed new machine tools, for example for cutting clay more precisely. In design he followed the current taste away from the Rococco (18th century, elaborate but graceful) towards the neo-classical. An amusing quote comes from one of Wedgwood's letters: *"13th Sept 1767: French and frippery have jingled together so long in my ideas that I scarcely know how to separate them!"*

He commissioned John Flaxman to design draperies *"to make nymphs and shepherds decent"* for *"Georgian neo-classicism did not extend to Athenian nudity!"* (from Godfrey Map 1898 -see bibliography)

Between 1774-1790 the finest plaques and cameos, and later vases and other ornamental items, were made at Etruria and exported all over the world. In 1782-4 a Boulton and Watt steam engine was installed to drive the clay, flint and colour mills. In 1792 a new 10 hp steam engine was ordered and in 1802 Josiah II bought a 30 hp engine. When his father died in 1796, he had taken over the works, and though retiring to the country for a short while, leaving his cousin Thomas Byerley in charge, he soon returned and continued working until his death in 1842.

The Wedgwood firm did not begin to produce fine china until the time of the Napoleonic Wars, under Josiah II, from 1811-12. Times were difficult on account of the turbulence in Europe, but Wedgwood ware found its way into Russia, Germany and Italy, and even into Turkey where smoking apparatus (chibouques and hookahs) made in Etruria sold well! This gives a good idea of the Wedgwoods' ingenuity and business acumen. In 1815 the Government ordered a dinner service and a large assortment of other pottery, for the use of the exiled Napoleon on the island of Saint Helena in the South Atlantic, at the immediate wish of the Prince Regent. The dinner service was white and gold with beautifully executed landscape scenes of England. Some of the ware was decorated with the 'Embossed Ivy Leaf' design and a popular legend grew in the 20th century that the pattern used was 'Napoleon Ivy'. During the 1950s and 60s the firm used a backstamp which promoted the romantic idea: *"Napoleon Ivy as used by Napoleon at St. Helena 1815"*. This pattern, of which I have an attractive tea service myself, is still used today.

The old Etruria Inn, 19th century engraving.

Early 20th century views of the Etruria potworks.
Above: View towards the canal bridge over the main road.
Below: This picture shows the subsidence of the works because of undermining.

After Josiah II died his younger son Francis inherited the estate. The 1840s proved to be a time of great difficulty because of a general slump in trade, and Francis was obliged to put the village, factory and hall up for sale. It must have been a sad time for the owners and workers alike. The catalogue of sale read:

To be sold at auction at the Castle Hotel, Newcastle-under-Lyme,
on Tuesday 13th. August 1844, at noon in lots:-
Etruria, in the Staffordshire Potteries, a capital mansion called 'Etruria Hall' with 44 acres
of turf land and surrounding same, interspersed with ornamental timber...
A complete estate of about 45 acres, called Ridge House Farm, presenting
an admirable situation for a villa residence.
Also an extensive and complete set of pot works known as Etruria Works
situate on the banks of the Trent and Mersey Canal.

Fortunately it proved impossible to find a buyer for the works, and most of the estate passed back into the hands of the Wedgwood family. The bill of sale continued:

Iron Foundry and Machine Works adjoining said canal.
In addition more than 100 houses and shops comprising the whole village of Etruria,
through which the turnpike road from Newcastle to Leek passes.

Francis Wedgwood worked hard and proved to be the saviour of the Etruria Pottery! He managed to carry on by taking partners who were able to put some capital into the works. It thankfully survived. Between 1850-80 there was a great increase in power, with steam pumps, clay filter presses and blunger and pug mills for the preparing of the clay. There were power driven jiggers and jollies (happy sounding names) for shaping the ware.

Ten years later economic depression again affected the pottery industry, because earthenware had begun to be produced in America, and Wedgwood suffered heavy losses. However, Josiah Wedgwood and Sons Ltd were world famous and when the upturn came, they were ready, as can be seen from an old newspaper cutting about the firm supplying President Theodore Roosevelt with a service of 1,800 pieces for the White House, Washington, in 1902!

In more recent years, Wedgwood supplied the service for one of Queen Elizabeth's Coronation Banquets in 1953 and in the following year made the City of Manchester's new Civic Service of 3,038 pieces. Prestigious orders indeed!

The Etruria works had become prone to subsidence because of mining and also damp from the canal, two branches of which went right into the factory. The long frontage bordering the canal sank below the level of the water (by 1960 to the dangerous depth of 12 feet!) In 1897 much repair work was needed to the buildings, and local collieries and the Duchy of Lancaster were involved. Mining below the works stopped but the subsidence did not. In 1907 more building took place and electricity was installed in the works. Even so it could not have been a comfortable place to work in by this time.

Etruria Hall had been let to Earl Granville, owner of the ever increasing Iron and Steel Works nearby, as early as 1849. In 1949 the whole site was sold to the Steel Works, the Wedgwood Pottery Firm having already partly moved to their new country setting at Barlaston at the end of the 1930s. In October 1940, 400 of the 1,000 employees went to work at the new, all electric factory (the first such pottery in the country) on the production of fine earthenware. The first 20 workers' houses of the 100 planned were already built and 4,000 trees had been planted in the planned development of this beautiful 'garden village'.

The Wedgwood family still owned part of the Etruria site until the 1940s, though from the mid 1800s more and more of the land had been developed for heavy industry, isolating the potworks amongst slag heaps and belching chimneys and furnaces, the hall completely blackened by grime.

One of the last uses made of the old Wedgwood buildings was as a depot for the Dunlop Rubber Co. and finally as a storeroom for electrical control panels for the steel works during 1961-62, prior to their installation in the new integrated steel making plant being built on land to the west of the canal, close to Middleport.

The pottery works were demolished in 1965, sadly just before the policy of saving historic buildings came into being. Ironically too, the steel making plant, which began operating in 1964, was shut down in 1978 and demolished in the 1980s.

A postcript of information comes from an acquaintance whose grandfather worked at the old Etruria potworks in the fine china section reintroduced in 1876, and who showed me a photo of him and other workers in 1882. Grandfather and his family had lived in one of the Wedgwood cottages at Etruria but had moved to a larger house in Basford, when his children numbered twelve! He spoke of a hospital for Wedgwood workers at Stoneyfields which was a large house on the main road into Newcastle (near to the present New Vic Theatre) run by Dr. Bent whose home it was. This building is now the public house known as the 'Polite Vicar' after the Rev. Ian Gregory, founder of the body known as 'The Polite Society'.

The round tower at the left end is all that remains today. By Alf Wakefield.

The Wedgwood factory at Barlaston - the first fully electric pottery works in the Country.
Below the Stoke on Trent area and places that are a must for the tourist.

Six
ETRURIA HALL

Etruria Hall has been at the centre of the site in its 250 year history, the nucleus for thousands and thousands of jobs and peoples' lives. The Ridge House was demolished and the new residence for the Wedgwood family built lower down the valley of beautiful red brick, every one made by hand. It was designed by Joseph Pickford of Derby and cost £22,000. Positioned directly north to south, it faced the valley between Hartshill and Longton, and overlooked the new factory and village. The famous building is still a magnificent sight, surrounded by the Moat House Hotel, as one looks downhill from the top of Basford Bank -the road from Newcastle-under-Lyme and the old turnpike road of Josiah I's day.

The Hall was ready for occupation by 11th November 1769 and Josiah and Sarah Wedgwood entertained 120 employees at a party in Burslem Town Hall to celebrate. Their new home had many lovely rooms, as well as entrance and staircase halls. There were large, dry cellars underneath, where Josiah was to do much experimenting to improve his pastes, ceramic colours and glazes.

Sadly perhaps for romantic souls the popular notion of a secret tunnel from here to the works has been discounted, though given some credence by Ernest Warrilow in his 1952 *History of Etruria*. In the 1930s the caretaker at the Hall showed a young office lad named Les Hall a passage some 60 feet long, where he said the wine had been kept. This went off the cellar to the south. Much later, when Les was an electrical engineer for the steel works, he designed a new sub-station which was to go exactly over where this particular passageway was supposed to have continued. The chief works engineer gave orders that the whole area should be dug by hand - just in case! This was a tremendous task for the bricklayers as the area measured 40 foot square by 40 foot deep! No evidence which might have indicated the existence of a secret

The bricked up tunnel entrance in the cellar of Etruria Hall. It was 60 feet long and used to store wine.

passage was found - so the old myth was dispelled. In my research other tales of secret passages have surfaced in different locations ....I guess we are all romantics at heart!

Inside the Hall the rooms were decorated with terracotta bas-reliefs and stained glass, the ceilings were neat and unostentatious, and the Adam fireplaces were set with fine Jasper plaques. The salon housed a collection of beautiful objets d'art and vases, and the library was lined with books from floor to ceiling. The family loved music and had a fine harpsichord in the music room, and a hired barrel organ was sent for the children by Mr. Bentley.

They were a large and happy family and often entertained as many as 20 children outside on the lawns. Behind the house were outbuildings and stabling for 14 horses and a shed for 12 cows. There were kitchen and flower gardens and excellent pasture and meadowland. The bleak countryside had soon been converted by skillful planners with advice from experts like Capability Brown, introduced to Wedgwood by the Duke of Bridgewater. 900 trees were brought from London and planted round the Hall for protection against the wind, and a beautiful grove lined the road from the rear of the house to the Lodge situated at the bottom of Cobridge Road.

In 1794 the servants of the Wedgwood family were numerous: butler, footman, groom, coach postillion, gardener, housekeeper and many maids. Illustrious guests came to the house, including artists like George Stubbs, who painted a picture of the couple with seven children, in the grounds of their home in 1780. This is now held in storage at Barlaston by the Wedgwood Trust, as are other works of art including portraits by Sir Joshua Reynolds, until the opening of the Museum scheduled for 2002.

When Josiah I died in 1795 the house stood empty for a spell before being occupied by Thomas Byerley for a short while. In the late 1820s it became a school under a Dr. Magnus for a couple of years. In 1842 Mr and Mrs Francis Wedgwood lived there for a time. Heavy industry had begun to creep into Etruria as early as 1824 and gradually the beauty of the place was eroded, though it was still quite lovely around the Hall at the aforementioned sale in 1849.

In 1858 work started on the foundations of the vast steelworks to the west of the Hall, although there was a reprieve when one of the Shelton Steel works's partners, Colonel W.S. Roden, occupied the Hall in the 1850s. He was Commander of the Etruria Volunteers, whose canons he placed in front of the Hall. He was much loved and respected by the people, for he took a great interest in them and in the whole area. He later became Mayor of Hanley and subsequently MP for Stoke-on-Trent.

Etruria Hall and the surrounding parkland were still lovely in 1864 despite a line of the railway serving the steelworks passing straight in front of it - strawberries and roses could still be bought at the house. However smoke and fumes were beginning to spoil the vegetation and the outlook was dreary. A great pit mound began to grow behind the Hall, though in front the lawns were always kept beautiful. In 1880 the Hall stood empty for a while, and then was let as tenements. From at least 1892 it was used as offices by Shelton Bar, who eventually bought the building from the Duchy of Lancaster in 1932. They sited their main entrance at the back, that is the eastern side, of the building.

Quickly now Etruria Hall lost its beauty as it acquired a thick coating of black smoke and grime which it was to retain until the 1980s! About 1916 a further large wing was added on the Shelton side and much interior alteration took place at this time.

Inside, the boardroom and offices on the second floor were kept beautiful and they had open Adam fireplaces even in the 1930s. A pottery jug to comemorate the first "blowing in" of Shelton's furnace in January 1841 was kept in a glass case there. In this historic building my father spent many of his working hours redecorating the different rooms. I wish he could see it now in its restored elegance.

Seven
1995 -- CELEBRATION YEAR

1995 was the 200th anniversary of Josiah Wedgwood's death, and special exhibitions and celebrations took place, including a display of about 250 pieces of the famous Russian 'Frog' service in London. These were valued at an astonishing 6 million pounds! A local event was the delivery of a lecture on *The Man and his Work* by the Curator of the Wedgwood Museum, Gaye Blake-Roberts.

12 EVENING SENTINEL, Wednesday, June 7, 1995 _____**NEWS**_____

A NEW EXHIBITION IN LONDON HIGHLIGHTS THE SKILLS OF POTTERS

The genius of Wedgwood

A MAJOR exhibition on The Genius of Wedgwood opens on Friday at the Victoria and Albert Museum in London.

Priceless examples of Josiah Wedgwood's craft have been assembled from all over the world, including some from Russia.

Sentinel reporter PETER HOLMES and photographer NEIL HULSE travelled to London to see what is on offer.

JOSIAH Wedgwood died 200 years ago this year at the age of 65.

In his lifetime he is credited with inventing major improvements in the technology of the pottery industry alongside huge improvements in designs.

His aim was to produce pottery of the highest quality suitable for people from all walks of life.

The exhibition provides examples of the finest

● Wedgwood Museum curator Gaye Blake Roberts with one of Wedgwood's many triumphs, the biggest ceramic vase made in the 18th century

From the Sentinel 1995.

The time of Josiah Wedgwood I was one of the most interesting in all our Country's social history, the Industrial Revolution, when experiments and discoveries brought untold riches to men of means, with great changes in all spheres of industry, not least that of ceramics. Ideas and fashions changed rapidly, as many rich people travelled further afield because of better roads and more comfortable carriages. The life of the down-trodden poor, in contrast, was unbelievably hard - they worked in the vilest of conditions, their small children too, for extremely low wages which barely enabled them to survive.

It became fashionable for young men of substance to round off their education with a tour of Europe, accompanied by a tutor, and they returned with exciting stories, new ideas, styles and artifacts. There was a newly awakened interest in classical art, architecture, antiques, beautiful homes and gardens, and exotic fruit and plants from abroad. Rich families visited each other in a whirl of social events, vying with each other to provide the most dazzling and outstanding hospitality at their mansions. Wedgwood was in his element as he seized every opportunity to provide this new aristocracy with new styles of ware and all manner of interesting ceramics for their magnificent homes. It was held (by the rich of course) that *"elegance was the essential and governing factor of anything that was purchased."*

The perfection of the green glaze and production of cauliflower ware had brought great success. The design of the exotic, recently imported pineapple was extremely popular, much sort after and hailed as the symbol of hospitality. Real pineapples were stuck on the top of gateposts as signs of welcome to guests at parties, and the pineapple design was incorporated into stonework at entrances and on newell posts of stairs. Such decoration can still be seen today, for example at the entrance gates to Whitmore Hall, not far from Newcastle.

The other great triumph for Wedgwood at this time was the creamware, of which he had, with his typical astuteness and philosophy (when other potters had fought shy of a royal order) provided a tea service for Queen Charlotte, saying that he wished *"if possible (to) do in this as we have done in other things - begin at the Head first & then proceed to the inferior members."* After that he was pleased to be able to call himself *"Potter to Her Majesty"*.

Josiah was constantly trying out new and exciting forms to attract the public, his partner Bentley always encouraging him forward. Josiah was particularly fond of shells and it is recorded that he urged a friend on honeymoon (tongue in cheek no doubt) not to bother with other pursuits but to get himself onto the beach and find him such-and-such a shell! He produced lovely shell shaped dishes, especially for dessert services, and these were shown to perfection on highly polished tables, when the paraphernalia of the dinner and the cloth had been removed. At the time etiquette was very important and meals extremely formal. No expense was spared to put on the most sumptuous meals - indulgence knew no bounds. It was quite usual to have a commode, suitably surrounded by a screen, actually in the dining room, in case of need! The table setting was most important, and elaborate centre pieces were conjured up in a pyramid of fluted moulds filled with coloured jellies and syllabubs. When the moulds were removed the jellies dazzled the eyes with reflections of the candlelights and the sumptuous fare!

The new interest in plants and gardening brought a demand for pots and vases, and Wedgwood seized the opprtunity to produce all kinds in great number, some imitating natural substances like porphyry, marble and agate. These were far cheaper at 34 shillings than the real thing and sold in quantity. He presented a number of these to the Duchess of Devonshire, and from then on 'Devonshires' became the term for such vases - the canny businessman's brain seemed always to be at work! (It is said that the great man only needed four or five hours sleep). He produced busts to be placed in the now highly fashionable libraries of great houses, as well as plaques and tiles to delight the eye in rich men's salons, dining rooms, halls and kitchens. Wedgwood wooed his lady customers with his products at his fashionable showrooms in London, where rich society and the intelligentsia met. It was an exciting and exhilarating time for the rich and powerful.

For the poor and wretchedly overworked ordinary folk it was another matter entirely! However, it was noted by no less a person than John Wesley that Josiah Wedgwood cared for his workers. He said he had met a man in the Potteries by the name of J Wedgwood who was interested in his workers, their health and their welfare! He made them wash their hands and faces and change their clothes after working in clay. Wesley said, *"His soul is close to God"* We are also indebted to the founder of Methodism for the only accurate description that we have of Wedgwood, *"a man of small stature and lame."* Where Wesley met Wedgwood is unknown - there is no record of him visiting Wedgwood in the firm's archives! It would probably have been at one of Wesley's open air meetings that he spotted the famous potter.

The Throwing Room at the Ornamental Works Etruria in the early 19th century,
and below inside the potworks in the early 20th century by Alf Wakefield

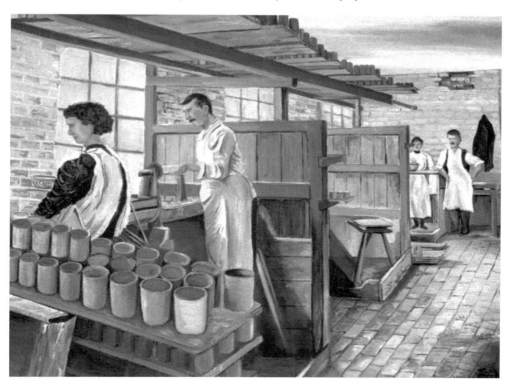

1898 Ordnance Survey

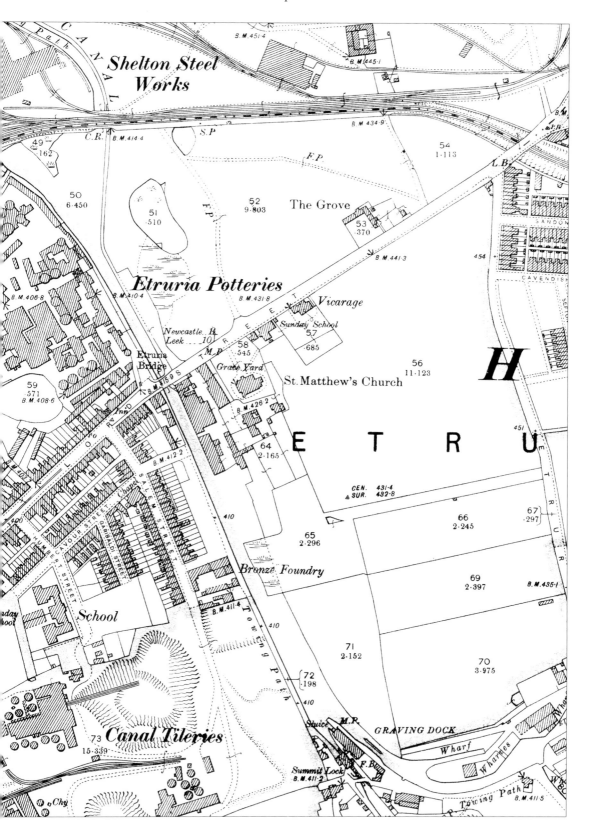

Eight
THE LAST FEW YEARS OF WORKING AT THE ETRURIA POTWORKS

It was a great pleasure a few years back to meet a very lively octogenarian from Dresden (near to Longton) who had vivid memories of her work at the old Wedgwood potworks in the first half of the 20th century, before it was closed down completely. Her name is Elsie Wardle and she thoroughly enjoyed reminiscing.

Jobs were scarce in the 1930s and at 20 Elsie was out of work. If you had had a job before you were out of work you received 10 shillings a week dole money for 10 weeks, but after that nothing. Elsie wanted to go to church, having been recently converted, but, she said, *"I'd only got tuppence, a penny for the church plate and a penny for the bus. So I decided to walk. I thought, 'It's all I've got, Lord, so You can 'ave it. You can do more with it than I can!' So I got 'ome a bit late and Mother wanted to know why. I said, 'Oh, bus was late.' But, yer know, he's looked after me ever since - me sister was waiting for me when I got 'ome, to tell me there was a job for me at Wedgwood!"*

This sister lived next door to the head mouldmaker at the works and he had got her the job. It was 1932 and Elsie remembered vividly and with real enjoyment her work as a cup handler there. Wedgwood had a big order in from Cadburys for mugs which they were giving away free with their new 'Bournvita', and she worked first on these, being an experienced cup handler already. The order was very welcome since the firm was struggling to keep going at the time.

Methods were quite traditional at Etruria, she recalled, for they still used an iron tube called a 'dod', into which clay was pushed and came out in long strips. These were cut to the necessary size for handles and then shaped by hand. For chinaware, slip (liquid clay) was poured into moulds to make the two halves of a handle. The work was hard and physical, for you had to press the two halves of the mould together in the fold of your tummy! Sometimes though you didn't bother but just banged them together with your hands! A far cry indeed from today's automation.

Elsie at work at Wedgwood

Elsie actually introduced them to a method of making 3 handles at once, and later 12, though at first they wouldn't believe it was possible. She assured them that it was because she had done it at another potbank. Needless to say she received no remuneration for this, credit going to the incumbent mouldmaker.

Elsie was the only girl kept on in her shop after the Cadbury job was finished, and she was transferred to the chinaware shop, which was in a long army-style hut, right next to the iron and steel works. No-one was allowed to smoke there because it affected the surface of the ware, and I imagine that the windows must have been kept tight shut too, on account of the dust laden air from the steelworks.

She worked well and was soon teaching other girls the art of handling. She was not paid for this, but her *"time was made up"* - for when she was not handling herself, as they were paid piecework. When the cups were done they were carried on long boards held over the shoulder, about 3 dozen cups or so at a time, into an extension called the greenhouse (a name I think common to potworks for where unfinished ware was placed). Elsie recalled that sometimes the wind whipped down the Etruria valley and straight through the works, and one day this happened just as a girl emerged outside with her board at the top of the stairs. The wind whipped it from her shoulder and sent it flying into the air, cups and all! The very strict forewoman gave the poor girl a terrible telling off, using foul language, though it hadn't been the girl's fault at all. Elsie felt very sorry for her.

The cuphandlers with their boards by Alf Wakefield.

The men never considered the women as good as themselves and when Elsie heard a remark to this effect one day, she retorted cheekily as she passed with her board of cups; *"A (I) did that lot a bit quicker, didn"t a?"* She heard one of the men say, *"'er mustav 'eard worra said."* Elsie chuckled as she remembered - it was unheard of for a girl to be cheeky then, but she added, you had to stick up for yourself to receive just reward for what you did.

Some of her work was on creamware soup dishes which required two handles, and great precision was needed to place these exactly opposite to each other. She became so proficient that she was able to do the work without even marking beforehand! When Prince Philip came to visit the factory at Barlaston, Elsie was chosen to demonstrate for him. She said she was not in the least bit nervous, and when the Prince said, *"It beats me how you know where to put them on!"* unembarrassed she replied, *"Oh, it's just a matter of getting your eye in."* (December 1951 when the Prince came to open the Ceramic Research Centre at Penkhull).

Elsie couldn't remember how many people worked at Etruria in the last days, but she could remember every single person's name and the job each did! So we counted up together and worked out that there were still about 50, who had stayed on when the rest of the factory moved to Barlaston! Working conditions were tough at the time, the wind whistling through the works. The floors were made of blue bricks, or cobbles, and the only heating came from the stoves for drying the ware which ran down the middle of each shop. However the workers were happy and sang a great deal. The people in the individual shops had a friendly bond with each other; Elsie remembered with pleasure how they would pile up flowers and small gifts on the bench of anyone whose birthday it was, or perhaps they would play tricks on them. She recalled how one man who lived in the country would often bring bunches of wild flowers for the girls. Another, the head platemaker, used to bring her *The Young Soldier*, the Salvation Army newspaper, which he had bought in the pub - he said she could probably make better use of it than him!

She listed the various jobs at the potworks; clay carriers, mould runners, thrower and assistant, slip maker and assistant, turners, platemakers, handlers, lookers-to-the-ware, placers, firemen, biscuitware workers, and a title that intrigued me - the 'towing lady'. This person used a piece of hemp, or "tow", to rub round the edges of a plate to remove any roughness. Then of course there were the ancillary workers, like the canteen lady and her helpers, and the bath lady.

In the canteen the employees could have a hot dinner and pudding for 5d, which they could eat there or back in their own workshop, although many people, including Elsie, took sandwiches to work because it was much cheaper. During World War II the factory canteen served dinners to the childen from Etruria School. They were served at noon and the workers at half past. Elsie remembered the classes of children trooping past her workshop windows every day on their way to the canteen. She thinks this continued until rationing ended in the early 1950s. How the first Josiah would have approved!

There were bath houses provided for the workers, whether they dated from the founding of the village I do not know, but it would not surprise me, so thorough was the great man! They were situated away from the buildings, somewhere near to the Forge Lane which was about the middle of the village. Soap and towel were provided for 1d and folk had one bath per week, during the dinner hour, women on Mondays, Wednesdays and Fridays, and men the other days of the week. The lady in charge was the mother of the clay earthenware manager.

There was a 'seconds warehouse' where workers could buy pottery at a reduced rate. The man in charge was rather dour and had a sick wife. He would allow people to buy all they had selected only at his own whim. Someone whispered to Elsie that it helped if you asked how his wife was. She did this and found that ever afterwards she was allowed to buy all she ever selected!

As well as some interesting ware to remind her of her days at Wedgwood, Elsie possesses other mementoes, including several brass dockets which were used when you collected your wages. This must have been common practice, for Shelton Bar used a similar method, also for clocking on and off with.

Elsie recalled that the steelworks employed two very small ladies as, of all things, brickies' labourers, who had to wheelbarrow loads of bricks to the men relining the furnaces! They also took the men their tea and ran errands for them! It was at the time of the War and women had to fill the empty jobs.

The Wedgwoods were caring employees; Elsie recalled Mrs Cecil Wedgwood bringing a pair of clogs for a lad named Jimmie Boswell, from Halmerend. She gave parties for the workers every year at her house in Moddersall, lovely it was, Elsie remembered, with cakes and lemonade. At the time the directors of the firm, Mr Josiah, Mr Tom and Mr John, would sit down with the workers in the canteen for the Christmas party.

Elsie rmembers that, when the foundation stone was laid for the new works at Barlaston, Queen Mary visited the Etruria works. As the royal carriage was leaving, the workers climbed onto the canal wall to wave and cheer. Mr Josiah was spotted amongst them and he was invited into the royal carriage, and the workers cheered all the more!

Elsie, who will be 90 in June,2002, says she has a 'long' memory for the past but not a short one for today! She is still in touch with some of her 'cuphandler' friends of more than 70 years ago: Jean Weller (now Mrs Kesteven who lives in Hartshill) was the girl whose cups blew away on the top of the outside steps at the Wedgwood potworks, where her father, Sam Weller, was slipmaker in the earthenware (common clay) department; Kath Myatt (now Mrs Bould); Ethel Nixon from Salem Street, Etruria; Frances Evans; and Joyce Leigh who married a yank named Charlie King (now deceased), and lives in North Carolina, America. There was Lily Rowe who helped in the production of the utility Bournvita mugs. Elsie remembered that during the war, when 'Lease-Lend' was in operation with America, loads of these mugs were used as ballast in ships going back to the US. Mr Jack Farmer was the head platecaster, a very kind man who used to bring Elsie the Salvation Army papers, *The War Cry* and *The Young Soldier*. There were Mr Cook and George Pedley in this department.

Dave Titley was the head turner, and Elsie remembered him coming to work absolutely furious one day, because of the noise his neighbours in Milton had been making - presumably he had been unable to get his 'beauty sleep'. There is an interesting bit of history attached to this tale, which many local people will recall. It happened towards the end of the 1930s that a great Christian Revival Campaign was staged in the Potteries by Pastor Edward Jeffries, assisted by Pastor Griffiths who lived next door to the irate Dave. Meetings were held in all the Potteries' Town Halls and there was great fervour and interest, people flocking to hear the preaching and to seek healing. Dave said furiously *'It is all a load of tripe!'* Elsie remembered how she had prayed for the right answer to give him, and said quietly with a grin, *'Well, Dave, tripe IS very good for the stomach!'*

She told me then how a friend of hers, Doris Reynolds (who had been a decorator at an old pottery called Salisbury china works) had received a marvellous healing experience through Pastor Jeffries' prayer. She had one leg 5¼ inches shorter than the other and had worn callipers for years, not from birth but due to an early attack of measles. She felt a tremendous warming in her knee, a 'quickening' she called it, as he prayed for her, removed her callipers and found that the leg was 2 inches longer. She never wore the callipers again, and eventually the leg was only ½ an inch shorter than the other, and she was able later in life to wear ordinary shoes! No doubt today's doctors would understand better the condition, yet we can imagine the joy of her and the many other people who became better from their ailments.

The china slipmaker at Etruria was Mr Ken Morrall and his assistant was Mr Bill Machin. The china mouldmaker was Mr Charlie Porter. China casters were Percy Rowe, George Hedley and Abe Cook, an old fashioned bachelor - the latter two were always at loggerheads! The bath lady was Mrs Jinks, and her son, Billy Jinks, was earthenware clay manager. The forewoman 'looker-to-the-ware' was Miss Allman of Newcastle, whose office was always called the 'potting office'. No-one ever knew her christian name.

Mr Tom Woodwood from Hanley was a placer. One of the firemen for the bottle ovens was always called 'Black Joe' because he looked filthy most of the time. He was odd-job man-around too, and his was hard, dirty work, and very hot.

Albert Deaville, who had demonstrated to my husband as a schoolboy the application of the white moulds to Jasper ware, did this job for many years. He played cricket with him in later life. Albert lived in Hartshill and was a keen gardener. He now lives in sheltered accommodation in the nearby countryside.

Eric Weller (Jean's brother) was general earthenware turner. Another thrower, whose name Elsie could not remember, got killed in a road accident in Longton. He had a buxom, old fashioned lady assistant, who always wore a clean white overall and apron. Miss Geen was head of the canteen; her father was an alderman and had been mayor.

Elsie said that there had been a place ready for all of the workers in Etruria at the new Barlaston factory, but when the war began part of it had been taken over by the government for the making of aircraft screws. She said they were a happy bunch of workers, though if they were 'franked' (late for work), they were not allowed on the works by the lodgeman, but had to lose a day or half a day's work. They were very fond of their bosses, especially Mr Tom (Wedgwood), who was always willing to take off his jacket and work alongside any of the workers in the factory - they were just trying to get going with china manufacture again and it was his 'pet' scheme.

The sister and wife of Bill Eaton, mentioned in the Shelton Bar section, Ethel and Alice, also still recall with zest their early girlhood in Etruria, and the fact that when they reached the age of 14 or 15 they both found work as enamellers at the Wedgwood factory in Barlaston.

Nine
POSTSCRIPT ON HANDLING

Some interesting information about 'handling' comes from the book *When I was a Child* by Charles Shaw, a Potteries man who had worked in the industry as a child labourer in the 1840s. This book is a most significant local history, written by a deeply sincere and caring man. Charles Shaw was born in 1832 and began working in a potbank at Burslem at the tender age of seven! He began writing his experiences when he was about sixty and his book, was first published in 1903.

His first job was as mould runner, his second that of handler, a less arduous though still exacting job for a small boy, and he worked from 70 to 80 hours a week!

For making handles, mostly for tea cups and porter mugs, there were two half moulds, made to fit together by notches on one and holes on the other. The piece of clay for the handle was placed in the bottom half, the top put on and pressed down by the boy's stomach *"with a sort of wriggle"*. This ties in well with Elsie's description. The clay for the handles was put into a round iron box with a die at the bottom, through which the softened clay was forced by a large metal plate worked down the box by a screw on a long handle. The clay came out like a tapeworm, varying in thickness according to the size of the die. For small mugs, called 'cans', handles were made by hand, twisting the piece of clay in an 's' shape and applying it with slip.

The child worked below ground level, with no ventilation or light other than a small candle which had to be snuffed out at once if an overseer came round, and the child had to remain silent until he had gone! The child labourers were witness to scenes of the utmost debauchery, for there was little in the way of discipline or supervision in these awful works.

The mould runner's job was even more exacting. The little lad worked with the 'muffin' maker - muffin being the name for small plates less than 7 inches in diameter. The moulds for these were plaster casts, the clay being laid on with the wet right hand like a pancake, and tooled to make edge and rim while spun by the left hand. Then the cast had to be carried, at the run, by the boy helper to the stove room. This was about 4 or 5 yards square with a central drying stove, usually red hot, which provided the only light in the room. He had to place the mould on shelving which went all round the room in tiers, leaning against the wall so that the plate could receive the furnace heat without any damage to the soft clay. To reach the upper shelves it required wooden steps, which he had to run up and down. When plates were sufficiently dry they were carried back to the master to be 'tooled' or 'backed' on his whirligig to smoothe the outer surface. After that they were taken off to another store to be 'shelled off' the plaster mould, and the 'green' plates gathered in 'bungs' of about two dozen, ready for fettling, the least arduous job of the day.

The boy runners were literally kept running for 20 to 30 minutes at a time. Between there were other 'rest' jobs - small children like Charles Shaw had to 'wedge the clay' to make the clay workable they took a large lump, cut it with a wire, lifted half above the head and brought it down as hard as possible to mix with the other. This process was repeated over and over until the clay was of the consistency of putty!

These little souls would have little or nothing in their stomachs to sustain them throughout the day, so poor were the families they came from. The children were also responsible for lighting the stoves in the early morning, and had to find their own kindling! They were often in fear for their lives literally, so cruel were the masters, kicking and cuffing and cursing them, probably knowing no better, since they themselves would have been brought up in the same harsh 'school'. Shaw quotes:

> *"But the young, young children, O my brothers,*
> *They are weeping bitterly;*
> *They are weeping in the playtime of the others,*
> *In the country of the free."*

He worked in the potbanks in Burslem, the 'Mother Town' of the Potteries. Later he helped to make pottery 'toys' in a run down place they called 'the hell hole', where people lived and worked as well. He wrote that Josiah Wedgwood, the town's greatest son, had long since left the town, to do his brilliant work at Etruria, but the architectural and sanitary conditions there were not a world removed from those of Burslem: Josiah Wedgwood wrought marvels in the art of pottery, but righting the social evils was not yet of that time!

So said Charles Shaw. However, these views are those of a man who was not able to leave the bad conditions in which he himself had to work. We know that Josiah Wedgwood I and succeeding generations of his family did greatly improve the lot of all their workers. The gifted founder and caring, down-to-earth, family man could not have failed to have an effect on the society over which he ruled so benignly.

Two illustrations from the illustrated *When I Was a Child*.
Above: Wakes trips by barge to Trentham.
Right: Boy labourer making handles.

Why USA stands for United Staffordshire Appreciators . . .

●Hi y'all! Barbara Synos, Carole Fozkos, Carol Olejnik, and Kathleen Pucalik. Picture: DAVE RANDLE

We're just crazy about your pots

American Wedgwood enthusiasts appear in the Sentinel newspaper.

Left: Directions from Festival Park to the Visitors' Centre at Wedgwood, Barlaston. A trip by canal narrow boat is in the planning stage.

From the Evening Sentinel

Mr Herbert Cholerton gilding at Wedgwood in 1924 when the future George VI visited.

Plate, gold on black, part of a dinner service made for the British Exhibition in about 1951.

Ten
WORKERS IN GOLD

Mr Herbert Cholerton, born in the 1880s, worked at the Etruria potworks for 52 years as gilder and royal crest painter. Each member of the royal family has an individual crest, which is never available to the public. The photograph opposite, taken in 1924, shows Mr Cholerton at work, being watched by the Duke of York, later to become King George VI. Before the First World War Mr Cholerton worked on a complete set of dinner, dessert, tea and coffee service for the White House in America, which ran into more than a thousand items!

Mr Fred Cholerton, Herbert's son, was born in 1913 and followed in his father's footsteps as a gilder, beginning work aged 14 years in September 1927 at 11 shillings a week. He served Wedgwood for 51 years, retiring, as he fully intended, at the age of 65 in 1978. He served as a part-time fireman on the works, so through the Second World War he became a full-time fireman. He recalled that many deaf and dumb people worked at Wedgwood's since Lady Wedgwood was President of the Deaf and Dumb School at Penkhull. Fred lived at Penkhull and even at the age of 14 had an allotment where he worked every morning from 7am until it was time for work, when he would walk, or run, to Etruria!

Fred recalled that in the enamelling shop one side was devoted to decorating earthenware and the other to china. The boss was Miss Johnson, and she was very strict. 'Papa' Goodwin was the head of the design department and he, like Fred, lived in Penkhull. In the gilding of the ware Wedgwood always used the best gold which was extremely expensive. Fred warns people today to beware of adverts boasting of ware decorated with 24 carat gold, as this is too soft for pottery. Mostly 9 carat is used. At Wedgwood's they used 18 carat and this was ground at the works by the resident chemist, Mr. Floyd, and then mixed with the necessary oil ready for use. An assistant was caught pinching some of the gold dust, and putting extra fatty oil into the gold paint to make up the weight. He was sent packing of course. Another crafty way of stealing the gold was to wipe your brush on your apron, and then retrieve the precious stuff at home and sell it on. The gilders had to use special rags to clean their brushes, and these were gathered up and fired to redeem the gold, (Fred quoted the figure of £92's worth!). Most careful supervision was necessary to make sure that no-one pinched any of the rags!

As time went on important changes were made in the Gilders' shop to eradicate any dust, for one speck fired into the ware would spoil it. A specially painted concrete floor and anti-dust sliding doors, as well as special windows, were installed to keep the atmosphere as clean as possible. This was especially important with highly prestigious and expensive orders. Fred gave some interesting examples of such orders in the 1950s. Wedgwood were asked to produce a dinner, coffee and tea set for a 'British Week' exhibition in America. The designer for the ware was Mr James Hodgkiss (see following chapters). He named his designs after places he had visited and liked, (the first Josiah would have liked that idea Fred commented), and he called this ware 'Astbury'. It was on a black background, and was a highly complex design in raised gold, which he knew would take a very long time to apply. Fred doubted there would be sufficient to complete the order. However the management pressed him, and he decided to make an assessment of how much time and effort would be required (in other words a 'time and motion' study - an important concept in the labour market at that time). He worked out that if he laboured from 5.30am to 7pm for 6 days a week for a month, he could do it in time for the exhibition. He calculated that his arm would do 2½ miles each day moving at 32 mph. Fred used brushes of 6 sable bristles which he made himself.

At nearly 89 years of age Fred Cholerton was able to give me these intricate details without the least hesitation, his memory being entirely undiminished, as was his sense of humour. He grinned as he said that folk did not think the ware would sell because of the black background, yet every piece had been sold within an hour of the opening of the exhibition! A 10" dinner plate is now worth between £400-500.

Fred said that Mr Harry Barnard (see following chapter), who was an important member of the Wedgwood 'team', also came from Penkhull. The fresh air of this village on a hill close to Stoke must be excellent for producing artists of a very high calibre!

In 1953, The Potteries Federation had a Queen's Coronation vase created, the firms working on this being Mintons, Wedgwood, Doultons, Crown Derby, Royal Worcester and Spode, the latter making the lid. This vase was between 3 and 4 feet tall and had the Queen's ten beasts depicted on it. Fred worked on the red dragon of Wales and the griffin of Edward, (he couldn't remember which Edward it was), on which there was much gold. There were 11 of these vases made for the dominions, one for America, and a number made for the main cities, especially in Scotland. The Queen's vase he believes is in the Tower of London, and in Stoke there is one in the Lord Mayor's Parlour and one in Federation House.

During the 1930s at Etruria Fred was given the job of showing visitors round the factory - he felt it was given as an incentive to stop you leaving the firm's employ - and he enjoyed this very much as he met many interesting people. One was a large, very imposing and well dressed politician named Mr Hore Belisher, later to become famous for his invention of 'belisha beacons', used at pedestrian crossings to this day! A second man, Tommy Lyth, also became a tour guide, and then one or two ladies joined the ranks. There was a large notice displayed in the factory forbidding workers to accept tips from visitors. One of Fred's mates said he always to refuse the first offer, but accept the second, which would be larger!

Fred remembered escorting two young men round the works, one of whom was very eager to try his hand at painting several colours on a plate. Fred promised to have it fired for him and told him to return in a couple of weeks to see how the colours had changed with the firing. The young man returned, and he eventually spent a fortnight with Fred, painting different species of ducks on nine plates, which the he edged in gold for him. This was the great naturalist and artist, Peter Scott.

Fred gave some details of other workers and their jobs, in particular, Fred Clay, who was a 'ground layer'. This involved laying oil evenly on a plate to be enamelled, and using a 'boss', i.e. a silk pouch filled with cotton wool, to move it (boss it) all over gently, levelling the oil. Then powdered colours were thrown onto the surface near a fan and the plate was given a shake so that the powder was spread evenly. The plate was then fired. Needless to say there was no protection for the worker, who must have inhaled much dust. The 'towing ladies', mentioned elsewhere, worked in even more danger, as they used hemp, or tow as it was known from towing rope, or sandpaper, to rub off bits from the biscuit ware. They were very poorly paid, as were all the labouring pottery workers, and Fred always felt very sorry for them as he considered their working conditions worse than the miners'.

He recalled with pleasure some of his workmates; there were six male gilders and five ladies, including Mabel Bostock and Hilda Winfield. One of the men was crippled and never moved from his bench all day. Another never ever took off his hat, because he had white hair and didn't want anyone to see it. One named Mr Shingler was a great 'card' who had some peculiar verbal habits. One of these was to say "chiboo" at regular intervals through the day, (his mates never discovered why), and another was that he pronounced every single letter separately in all words, for example, he went on holiday to Torkuway (Torquay), and a plumber always had his 'b' in. Skithers (scissors), however, went one degree further. I think this is a Potteries dialect interpretation of the word, as I've heard it elsewhere. 'Old Smithy' was a bachelor, who came to work in a bowler hat which he carefully stored under his bench, but always put back on whenever he went to the toilet. Along with all the hard work there must have been plenty of merriment!

In the period of 1945-50s, Fred was involved in the production of commemorative plaques for the various stages of the laying of the telephone cables under the Atlantic Ocean between England and the United States. Each of the 5 or 6 stages was marked with a plaque recording the progress, the same pattern being used but with a different coloured border, red, blue, green or yellow. It would be interesting to know where these historic plates are now.

Fred's father, Herbert, had been a very keen photographer and saw many interesting things. One of these involved a boatee on the canal which flowed into the works. This boatee had painted his name along one side of his barge, and planned to do so on the other. He presumed that since he had started at the rudder, he would do the same on the other side. He had a heated argument about this with his wife, who said he was wrong. However, he proceeded to do it his way, and when Herbert saw the result he was amused as he realised it was perfect mirror writing, everything backwards And Fred had the photograph to prove it!! Talented Etruria fathers, of course, were always right!

On top of all his other activities, Fred was a Scout all his life and he attended the World Jamboree in 1929, which took place in England.

The subsiding pottery with Shelton Bar's chimneys behind. Alf Wakefield.

The canal alongside Wedgwood's Etruria works. Alf Wakefield.

The traditional Potteries thrower.

Eleven
MR BERTRAM HODGKISS (b. 1906) - A Few Memories of Etruria

My father James Hodgkiss, following art training at Burslem and Kensington Schools of Art, went to the Wedgwood works as Designer and was there for the next twenty-five years. Probably outstanding among his achievements was the introduction of Powder Blue which is mentioned in several works on Wedgwood. It was a process which gave an effect lost in antiquity but seen only on very early Chinese ware. Makeig Jones, a colleague of my father, occupied an adjacent studio and used the effect as a base for many of her freehand ephemeral works. She was a spinster and a close friend of one of the Wedgwood daughters and as a boy I spent many hours watching her work on pieces which are now collectors' items.

The decorating department was on the upper floor of a two storey building, approached from the usual square by an exposed stone staircase and wooden handrail. The ware was carried in and out using long planks and on the head. An oddity in the square was a small foot bridge which apparently went over nothing - but there had originally been a channel which travelled from the canal, under workshops, into the Works. Besides carrying materials it was rumoured that, with the collusion of the boat people, the potters had also been supplied this way with ale!

One of my father's closest colleagues at Wedgwoods was Harry Barnard who, at the time I visited the factory, appeared to be largely involved in publicity and sales promotion, but he had also worked at Macintyres and it is probable that among the moulds which MacIntyres sold to Moorcroft, when they closed, would be some of Barnard's models. Barnard had an uncle who was an R.A.(member of the Royal Academy) and he gave me a Scottish landscape for a wedding present but unfortunately it is unsigned.

Barnard wrote the book *Chats on Wedgwood Ware* and he and my father, *Artes Etruria Renascuntae* (Arts of Etruria Reborn); Barnard wrote the script and my father did the pencil drawings which depict features in the Etruria pottery. I have a number of the original drawings and Wedgwoods have the rest. One which depicted the entrance to the works and which I have, was blown up and at one time surrounded the entrance to the museum.

When Josiah Wedgwood decided to leave Burslem where he was renting two works, one from his uncles, John and Thomas, and the other from one of the Adams, he bought a 350 acre site from a Mrs Ashenhurst, the land extending from Cobridge to the Newcastle-Hanley road. His works and the Etruria Hall only covered a small part, the rest being used for grazing.

When Josiah died none of his offspring were interested in taking on the business, and many had fled the district. A relative from the London showroom took over, but the factory came on hard times and the factory, land and hall were put up for sale. There were no offers near the asking price so the land was sold off separately to Earl Granville and the steel works were born. This soon became a giant which overshadowed and poured dust and fumes over Josiah's creations and it continued to expand and burst its boundaries. On the Hanley side it spread over the Cobridge Road, with a connecting railway link over the road and a barrier which rose and fell so continuously that it affected the traffic even in those early days - and much more later, right up to the 1960s.

The production of pottery with these foul conditions above ground and the subsidence underground led to the decision to move to the green land and clean air of Barlaston. By this time the firm was a limited company, the financial holding of the family much diminished. I only remember there being one shop in the village which Josiah built to house his employees, I seem also to remember seeing that the cost of each house to build was less than one hundred pounds. The shop sold nothing but Wedgwood ware and I was given to understand that Smallwoods who kept the shop had sole selling rights in the Potteries.

During the last war I was living in Basford when, while on warden duty, there was a raid and a plane loosed its bombs intending them for Shelton Steel Works. They were a mile short and demolished a row of houses. A piece from a bomb case landed on the roof opposite my house, broke a tile and ricocheed through my bedroom window and landing on the bedroom carpet. I kept it as a souvenir for a time.

One of my aunties married a man who on discharge from the army worked on the furnaces at Shelton Bar. They lived in Dundee Road and my uncle was an interesting character not wholly approved of by my mother. He had been in the regular army in a cavalry regiment and had seen service in the Africa. He and my aunt were childless and I appeared to be a favourite since I used to spend many week-ends and holidays at the house, which was in the shadow of the works.

Since my uncle worked shifts I was entrusted with taking him food while he was at work. The journey took me down Forge Lane, which led to a a dusty track and a public house at the foot of the canal bridge adjoining the Wedgwood works. This pub did a roaring all day trade with the apprentice boys fetching beer in enamelled buckets to satisfy the furnace operators. I cannot remember any restriction on entering the works - you just arrived amidst rows of trucks and weird steam engines with flattened boilers, each with a name. Everywhere was so busy you stood and stared at your peril! After crossing this labyrinth you arrived at the furnaces and then had to climb an almost vertical steel stair before arriving at a steel platform where facing you were the rows of blindingly hot furnaces. I don't think mother can have known I did this - I doubt if she would have approved.

The electric trams I took as a fact of life from a very early age but I never remember learning what I know now, that they had been preceded by first horse drawn, and then steam trams. I remember being able to sprint and catch one on the move without fear of other traffic. I vividly recall the day I was walking in a thick fog - not uncommon then - and I had just passed a sharp bend in the road, when I heard a peculiar roar behind me and turning saw what seemed like a thousand small insects racing after me. Out of the mist there loomed a tram which slithered to a halt on its side. The insects turned out to be the contents of the conductor's bag, but he and the others on the tram were shaken but miraculously unhurt!

Soon after the conclusion of the First World War, a local war broke out between tram and motor transport. Numerous ex-army drivers saw the opportunity of becoming capitalists and invested in what were literally charabancs with bench seats, entered on either side of the vehicle and having knee high doors. The conductor hung precariously on the side and swung from row to row collecting the coppers, his bottom at risk every time the bus passed a lamp post. The competition for passengers became fierce, each vehicle aiming to prevent the next from getting in first at each bus stop. In the end the tram company, seeing Armageddon looming, decided to buy the usurpers out and, in modern terms, rationalise the service.

Twelve
ARTES ETRURIAE RENASCUNTUR
(THE WORKS OF ETRURIA RESURRECTED)

THIS BOOK ON THE WEDGWOOD WORKS AT ETRURIA IS REPRINTED HERE IN FULL.
IT WAS WRITTEN IN 1920 BY HARRY BARNARD AND ILLUSTRATED BY JAMES HODGKISS,
SALES MANAGER AND DESIGNER RESPECTIVELY AT WEDGWOODS.

ARTES ETRURIAE RENASCUNTUR

JOSIAH WEDGWOOD, F.R.S.
1730–1795.

A RECORD OF THE HISTORICAL OLD ✕✕✕
WORKS AT ETRURIA AS THEY EXIST ✕
TODAY, FORMING AN UNIQUE EXAMPLE OF
AN EIGHTEENTH CENTURY ENGLISH FACTORY.

TOLD BY HARRY BARNARD. ✕✕✕✕ A.D.
DRAWN BY JAMES HODGKISS. ✕✕ 1920.

"ARTES ETRURIAE RENASCUNTUR" was the self-made motto with which Josiah Wedgwood christened his new works in 1769. Let us look upon the busy corners of these "new works" as he saw them. At once the question presents itself, is it possible? The answer is emphatically in the affirmative, for there are many workshops and benches to-day where the exact replicas of his famous productions are still being made under the self-same conditions. Of course, these old corners of the past are quickly passing away, giving place to new machinery and methods, and those that remain are becoming surrounded, and almost buried in some cases, by modern buildings. Yet it is quite true that for some of the finest handicraft the original environment cannot be surpassed. The atmosphere and tradition of the late eighteenth century, carefully and faithfully preserved through five generations to the present one of both master and man, is the real factor that enables the present-day production to maintain that high standard which the untiring energy and application of the original "Master Potter" set out to accomplish.

This record does not pretend to be a description of the processes of manufacture, but as the visitor passes through the workshops these will all be shown and explained, so it will be sufficient if we say something about each of the drawings which have been made to illustrate this booklet, and it is hoped that this will form a souvenir of the visit and retain much in an interesting form which otherwise might be lost for ever.

Etruria—Why did Josiah Wedgwood choose this name? The works, and the village he built about them to accommodate his workmen upon the newly purchased land which was formerly known as "The Ridge House Estate," were at that time outside the actual Potteries and in the beautifully wooded and pastured country on the road to Newcastle-under-Lyme, the ancient borough of John of Gaunt, "time-honoured Lancaster."

Here he removed some of his best workmen from Burslem to manufacture those classic triumphs of ceramic art, inspired by the lately exhumed Etruscan relics then being introduced into this country by Sir William Hamilton, who (when he became a resident in Italy, as envoy to the Court of Naples), being a man of genius, an enthusiast, and a lover of antique art, made judicious purchases and carried out excavations at his own cost, thereby adding materially to his fine collection of antiquities. This collection he generously opened to the world, resolving to make it an inspiration to the artist and to prove to the then modern civilisation its indebtedness to the older one. He employed the finest Italian and French artists to copy the masterpieces, and the Frenchman D'Hancarville to write the necessary letterpress. The result of these endeavours appeared in two volumes published at Naples in 1766 and two in 1767, masterly in every way, and which have never been surpassed. The proofs of the plates seem to have been scattered by Sir William among his own friends, one of whom was Lord Cathcart, who in turn lent some to Wedgwood. These inspired the "Master Potter" with new ideas for his work, and we soon find that he made elaborate plans to rival the fine products of Etruscan and Grecian ceramic art.

It was at this time that he was contemplating, designing, and building his new works and village, so that his whole mind was full of this desire, that the arts of Etruria should be born again in the home he was preparing for his ideal.

The present-day visitor to Etruria must use every faculty of imagination, for the scene in 1769 must have been one of great beauty. There is not a trace of the park-like surroundings of the works now left; the very contour of the country has altered, owing to the sinkage caused by the mining beneath of a later date. Huge pyramidal "shraff" heaps tower above all surrounding buildings, even the furnace chimneys. The village street at that time was a gentle slope to the works, and only began to rise more steeply through a delightfully wooded lane, where the trees met overhead, after it had passed the canal course. All is now disfigured, and forge, blast-furnaces, mine-shafts, and derricks predominate. Not a tree remains of the park which surrounded Etruria Hall, which Wedgwood built for his residence, and the Hall itself is shorn of its beauty and importance as a residence, being used as the offices of the Shelton Iron, Steel & Coal Co., losing itself among the furnaces, chimney-stacks, and great boiler-roofed casting sheds.

But amidst all this modern commercial pomp and progress one is still able to turn aside and get a glimpse of what used to be the glory and pride of Etruria, and which still retains its hold upon those of the sixth generation who work there, for the old pottery works of Etruria have an unbroken record of steady progress from father to son during a period of over a century and a half.

It is an interesting fact that when our King and Queen honoured these old works with a visit in 1913, Her Majesty said to an old workman, "And are you a native of the Potteries?" He replied with an inborn pride, "No, Madam; I am an Etruscan." This answer conveys a great deal to one who considers these expressions of local feeling and accounts to a large extent for the loyalty which exists for the masters, who also have a similar record of continuity.

The reproduction of a pencil drawing *(figure 2)*, which has been made from an old water-colour painting, will give a fair idea of the appearance of the country at the end of the eighteenth century. The works and village will be traced running along the

FIGURE 2

centre of the picture, Etruria Hall on the rising ground to the left, and to the right the house which Wedgwood built for his partner Bentley. Above, on the higher undulating hills, is seen Hanley Church and the Windmill, the latter long since gone. On this ridge are the Potteries proper, Stoke being to the right, hidden by the tree in the foreground, and Longton again beyond that; to the left, Burslem lies below the ridge in the valley. The haymaking or harvesting in the field in front of the works gives the rural touch as it was in that day, for we have no doubt the artist faithfully recorded what he saw.

Now, will the visitor, who, we hope, has thrown off a little at least of the twentieth-century smoke and inhaled some of the eighteenth-century atmosphere, turn off the roadway to the left, upon reaching the canal, and pass down the descending road to the lodge gates. These gates and Lodgehouse, only thirty years ago, were above the canal, and the whole works stood above the water-level, but the sinkage due to the mining mentioned before has wrought the difference.

The third illustration will give you a backward glance of the entrance on to the works at the present time, showing the frontage with the old belfry (cupola), where hung the bell which used to summon the workpeople to and from work. At Burslem, ten years before these works were built, where Wedgwood originally started as a master potter, he was the first who used a bell for this purpose, instead of calling men to work by blowing a horn, as the other potters did, so this somewhat elaborate and imposing "bell coney" (as it used to be called) was no doubt an innovation and a proud possession in these early days. We now turn to the left along a road running between old buildings and ovens to the other side of the works, farthest away from the canal, and come upon the "marl bank," where the many raw materials used in the preparation of the various "bodies" or clays, of which the different wares are made, are allowed to lie in the open and "weather" before grinding and mixing takes place. Here are china clay from Cornwall, ball clay from Dorset, flint-stones from France, Cornish stone, which is partially disintegrated granite, and others awaiting the time when they will be used, each requiring much crushing and grinding. In the case of the black flint-stone, which is a well enough known natural object on the seashore, and in chalky deposits, it undergoes a calcining process or firing in a kiln, from which it issues as a dense hard white stone, but rendered friable by the heat to which it has been subjected. It is then crushed by heavy iron hammers in a mill driven in these days by steam or electric power, but in the eighteenth century Josiah's mill was an effective but much more primitive contrivance.

If we raise one of those delightful old hand-wrought iron latches, which remain still on some of the doors *(figure 4)*, we can see this ancient piece of machinery *(figure 5)* with the original gearing which worked it. Notice at the top right-hand corner the cogwheel, with the double revolving arm attached, which, as it turned, lifted the perpendicular shaft and heavy chert-stone, letting it fall again at regular intervals upon the calcined flint

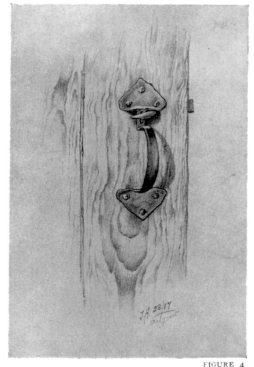

FIGURE 4

underneath in the hollow of the huge arm-chairlike receptacle, crushing it at each blow until the mass was reduced to tiny fragments, almost to dust. The very shafting which propels these cogwheels gives the age of the machinery, for circular shafting has superseded the square for over a century now.

This glimpse of the original works is along the ground floor of the old Mill-house, and the quaint old timber-work gives the suggestion of the durability that was intended by the designers and builders, and which has been fully realised by the present generation. We are told that these stout oak beams serve the purpose better than iron girders; they stand the strain more successfully, writhing and bending under pressure, returning again to the normal position under conditions that would cause iron to snap. Here, at least, jerry-building was not known. An old beam steam-engine that used to supply the motive power was originally built by Boulton & Watt, of Soho Works, Birmingham, and was on the "sun and planet" principle, afterwards altered to a crank motion in 1836 by the same firm's successors, but this had to give way to modern progress. Had it been less cumbersome, it would, no doubt, have proved an interesting relic for the Museum, but it had to be blown up by dynamite in 1913 to facilitate its removal.

Referring again to the sketch, the staircase at the left-hand far corner takes us to the first floor, where the grinding mills are. In these vat-like huge tubs the materials that go to form the different "bodies" are ground, large chert-stones being pushed round upon a stone bed at the bottom by strong wooden arms, and between these, for hours, days, even a week, the grinding and mixing goes on with water, so that the material in a slop or "slip" state is reduced to a thick, creamy liquid. This "slip" is next passed over a set of magnets, so arranged that they arrest any particle of iron it contains, for any left in the clay would cause brown specks or stains in the ware after firing. The "slip" then has to pass through fine silk lawns, 120 mesh being the

FIGURE

THE ORIGINAL FLINT CRUSHING MILL

usual gauge, which means that there are 14,400 holes to the square inch; any particles that will not pass this are arrested, and do not enter into the clay. It is then pumped into the clay press with great force. The clay press consists of a series of wooden trays or compartments, in each of which is a close textured cloth bag; the pressure is

FIGURE 6

continued long enough to squeeze out a large proportion of the water contained in the "slip," leaving the solid portions, which have been held in suspension, in the form of stiff clay. This is removed by taking the trays apart, opening the bags, and rolling up the clay, removing it to undergo another kneading and mixing in the "pug mill," a machine fitted with spirally arranged knives that cut and force the clay out through an aperture at the other end in a huge sausage of equal texture and consistency; this is cut off with a wire into convenient lengths for carrying away to the various potters' benches.

FIGURE 7

The old corner shown in *figure 6* is one where hand "blunging" was performed. Here the different materials were mixed in a tank with a large spade-like wooden pallet-knife, the mixture afterwards being poured into a flat stone trough with a fire underneath, the water evaporating away until it became clay of the right consistency. This process is still used for the smaller mixings of the more expensive clays used in the manufacture of the finest vases and decorated pieces in the Jasper wares.

Another interesting bit still remains *(figure 7)*, which shows an old mixing vat or wash-tub of another type worked by hand; the inlet and outlet for the "slip" are clearly seen.

FIGURE 8

Before leaving the mill we can look into the chemist's laboratory, where is the original shelf, with three carboys upon it *(figure 8)*, in each of which is reflected the old-fashioned small-paned window, one half of which is open.

The original iron mortar and pestle *(figure 9)*, used to crush small quantities of frit or stain, and which is still in use, is also here, as well as a copper pint measure *(figure 10)* of the same period.

A delightful contrivance for carrying "slip" about from one place to another is the two-wheeled truck *(figure 11)*, which lifted the full tub up, keeping it in a horizontal position; because it swung on two pivots, this was easily deposited again where required, and replaced by an empty to be taken away in the same manner.

FIGURE 9

FIGURE 10

On the same level is the hoist *(figure 12)* for raising or lowering materials between the ground and first floors. It is a very capable piece of mechanism. The working is simplicity itself, controlled by a single cord; the drums are of wood, fitted on an octagonal iron casting, each section being replaceable when worn out, the efficiency being as great as ever. It never gets out of order, and can lift any weight it is called upon to negotiate.

Before passing into the potters' shops, the exteriors of the buildings are worth more than a passing glance. The original plan of the works was rectangular, enclosing two spaces called the "White Bank" square and the "O.W." (Ornamental Works) square, the former surrounded by the workshops where the Cream Colour or Queen's Ware was made, and the latter by those of the Jasper and Basaltes Ware.

At each end of the frontage was, and still remains, though somewhat mutilated, a round tower with a dome roof, the centre of the building having a pediment with a clock, surmounted by the belfry. This is shown in the third illustration, where a partial view of the flanking tower at that end is visible. The other tower appears in *figure 13*, showing alterations at some later period when it was converted into an oven.

The buildings in the foreground were an addition to the 1769 plan, yet these are considerably over a century old, for under the left-hand warehouse one of the arms of the canal, which came round the older works, formerly ran. Here the barges passed on their way to unload the cargoes of clay, flint, and stone on to the marl bank at the rear of the works.

The remains of the old bridge form a distinct feature in this sketch, and one of the old yarns connected with it may be interesting. An old workman, who has now earned his last rest—for he worked at Etruria over sixty years—used to delight in telling the writer that, when he was a boy, he continually saw the rules disobeyed and the bargees bribed by a copious draught to smuggle an ewer full of beer on to the works during working hours for consumption in the work-shops, and has known a string to be passed along under the bridge just below the surface of the water, so that a half-filled bottle or can could be hauled backwards or forwards to an accomplice outside.

FIGURE 11

The windows in the building opposite us show four, if not five, epochs of workshop lighting, for that seen in *figure 36* is in the same block, though just hidden

FIGURE 12

from view by the projecting building at the right hand. It will be noticed that even this old relic superseded an earlier one which did not let in sufficient light for altered conditions of the work-bench inside. The primitive stay, with its wooden wedge-peg, passed through the wall, holding the lathe inside, an example of efficient home

ingenuity which has served its purpose for probably quite four generations.   This was
removed to make room for more modern requirements only last year.

The many quaint corners and outside stairways leading to various workshops on

FIGURE 13

the first floor are worth a recording note, as many have passed away in the short
period since the signing of the Armistice.   Reconstruction at Etruria has meant the
removal of many of these interesting links with the old workmen, whose feet wore
them into curves, and whose hands so materially assisted the great potter to accomplish
what was, and still remains, one of the world's greatest ceramic achievements.

THE "ORNAMENTAL WORKS" SQUARE   FIGURE 14

FIGURE 15

In *figure 26* is an upper and lower mould chamber. Here, though used every day, conditions allow grass, and even burdock, to maintain an undisturbed lodging.

The stairway in *figure 27*, even in 1916, was evidently only occasionally required; but this year it has again come into daily use.

Figure 28 gives a glimpse through a passage under one building to another beyond, while *figure 38* is quite a typical example of the way in which workshops cluster round and hug the oven hovels. An old pump is here. There were others in the old days, and also curious taps *(figure 34)* set in semi-circular alcoves, with a sink beneath, where workmen could place and fill a bucket or bowl. When water was carried by pipe to most of the workshops, these ceased to be used, and this, one of the few that have survived in a now out-of-the-way corner, has evidently proved a safe habitation for a spider.

Having lightly touched one or two points which will enable the visitor to pick out others for himself, we will pass through the archway beyond the cart in the sketch numbered 13, and find ourselves in the O.W. square, a view of which is shown in *figure 14*. We are now on the spot where all the finest masterpieces in vases, placques, and cameos were produced during the two marvellously productive decades embraced between 1770 and 1790.

The silhouettes in front of us are the "thrower" and his attendant. At this very spot the historical six vases were "thrown" by Josiah Wedgwood, while his partner, Thomas Bentley, turned the wheel on the 13th June, 1769, when these new works were opened. These vases were afterwards decorated with red upon the black basalte ground, with some figures from a frieze found upon one of the vases discovered by Sir William Hamilton, and the inscription upon the reverse side was, " Artes Etruriae Renascuntur." "One of the first day's productions at Etruria in Staffordshire by Wedgwood and Bentley."

The old wheel and bench are now no longer there, but it is recorded that when the woodwork was removed, the date 1769 was found upon a portion of it. The small-paned leaded window remained until about fifteen years ago. The handicraft of the "thrower" is perhaps the most fascinating of all the potter's art. It is the nearest approach to creation which is humanly possible, for from the soft, plastic ball of clay, he, with no other aid than a revolving disc, and his hands, eye, and brain, pulls up and forms with the yielding mass the shape which he desires. When pairs or numbers of the same are required, compasses, callipers, and inside and outside ribs, as they are

BLOCK ON WHICH ORNAMENTING MOULDS ARE MADE   FIGURE 16

FIGURE 18

called, are used to keep hand and eye under control. No description can take the place of a five-minute demonstration, however.

When the "thrown" pieces have left the potter's wheel, they are allowed to stiffen, and this partial drying process is often carried out in fine weather in the sunshine, as shown in the sketch, which helps to preserve the old-time feeling of the surroundings. Natural drying, when it can be resorted to, is always better, though a slower process, than artificial heat.

Previous to the visit of our King and Queen in 1913, a cobblestone pavement which covered this old courtyard was removed so as to make the rough places smooth for the Royal feet, but it has also removed some of the quaintness which was a delight to the artistic eye. Opening on this square, besides the "throwers'" shops, we have also those of the "turners." When the clay piece has attained the correct amount of stiffness, termed "green hard" (popularly

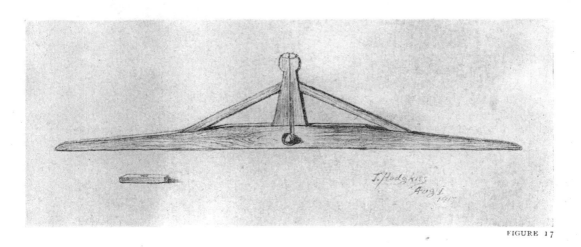

FIGURE 17

FIGURE 19

we can describe it as cheese hard), it is passed on to the "turner," who removes the outside roughness left by the "thrower's" hands, and cuts with special soft-metal tools, shaped by himself, beads, mouldings, and bands, giving the article its finished outline, burnishing afterwards with a polished steel tool the whole surface. If any coloured grounds or

FIGURE 20

bands, runner beads, checkered patterns, fluted or nulled surfaces, are wanted, it is at the "turner's" bench that the piece receives it.

Figure 15 shows the old tread-lathe, now supplanted by the motor-driven one, except for the very highest class of ornamental pieces, where absolute and minute control over the machine is essential, and where the "turner," completely the art workman, needs the whole attention of his brain and eye upon the work he is doing, without having to consider any contrivance for speed regulation. His "treader," always working by his side, soon gets into sympathy with all his requirements.

In this square still stands (like the old stocks in some country villages, outside the church) the grindstone *(figure 18)*, upon which the workmen ground their tools in the eighteenth century. As will be seen, it is worn down almost to the spindle, from a diameter which must have been originally about three feet, judging by the size of the opening in which it turned. The water trough has gone. As it is not in the way, it remains here, a link with the past, a silent record, a milestone on the roadway travelled.

FIGURE 21

FIGURE 22

Ascending the steps in the corner *(figure 14)*, we find in one of the upper rooms a little nook where some of the most important work has always been carried out, and here is evidence of the forethought of the master *(figure 16)*. This is not a block merely, but is the greater portion of the whole trunk of an oak tree, which passes through the floor and stands as a column in the workshop below, finding a firm foundation by bedding itself in the earth. An old workman years ago, who used to take visitors round, told the tale of the beautiful oak trees which grew on this estate, and how, when Wedgwood wanted to put up this particular building, was loath to destroy this one, and so built round it. Afterwards, when the tree died, its top was cut off and this table was formed in the upper shop. This recital was generally received with a polite smile, for the old gentleman really believed it was quite true, until one day a visitor, I think an American, made the cute remark by way of comment, to no one in particular, "Oh, I see, the trees grew root uppermost in this locality then!" This trunk was placed here, turned with the largest end up, and has always been used for making the clay moulds (afterwards fired into hard "pitcher") from which the fine Jasper figures and ornaments are pressed. As this necessitates much hammering with a wooden mallet to get all the parts of the delicate modelling very sharp, it would cause constant vibration of the building, to the annoyance of the ornamenters on the same floor; but placed as it is, the vibration is received by the earth, the noise being deadened very considerably also.

FIGURE 23

When the "turner" has finished his work, the piece, still in "green hard" clay, is passed to the ornamenter, whose assistant makes for him (in the "pitcher" moulds referred to) the figures or ornaments he requires, and with great dexterity he applies these clay ornaments to the piece, simply damping the surface with water, and using only finger pressure, so delicate that the finest detail of the modelling is not even marked by the texture of the skin. This is all that is necessary to remove any air-bubbles between the two clay surfaces and make them adhere, both in the drying and firing processes, if the work has been properly carried out. Opportunity will be given to see the ornamenter at work, and a peep into the "placing-house" will show the thoroughly dried ware, still clay, being placed into "saggars" before it is stacked up in "bungs" in the oven preparatory to firing. The inside of an oven can also be inspected, if not firing, and the care that is necessary at this last stage, when all the costly labour and time have been spent upon the work, will be appreciated. In the oven, the fire, the element, after all, only partially controlled, can, and does make or mar all the work that has been put upon the ware, baffling at times every effort to understand its mysteries.

There are a great many more very interesting details which one can pause to examine, but a few only must suffice, or this record will become too cumbersome, as it is not the intention, by any means, to make it exhaustive.

FIGURE 24

J. Hodgkiss
25/3/1919

In the Jasper warehouse, where the fired pieces are examined and sorted after coming from the oven, the effect in every respect must be almost as it was when the building was first erected; and here is an old safe *(figure 19)* built of stone slabs, lined with iron, having a door of the same metal, which is provided with quite a complicated lock. This is an early predecessor of the Chubb or Milner, and although it does not look very fireproof, it was no doubt considered to be a safe depository for any book or papers of value.

The little tablet *(figure 20)* on the door informs us that it was made by Slark, of No. 10, Cheapside, presumably London.

Another important piece of furniture which has survived is the grandfather clock *(figure 22)* in the engine-house, that probably regulated the working hours, and shows its authority by the inscription upon it, "Engine time" *(figure 23)*, evidently permitting no contradiction, for, if the engine stopped, naturally some portion of the work at least would have to cease also.

FIGURE 25

MOULD CHAMBERS   FIGURE 26

AN OLD STAIRWAY   FIGURE 27

Other useful pieces of workshop furniture still remain. Around each one can picture the old folks who daily used them—the more important foreman, or even the

G. Hodgkins
24/7/16
FIGURE 28

master, with knee-breeches and stockings, buckled shoes and wig, the heavy lapelled and collared coat with brass buttons, who would occupy the chair *(figure 24)* while he made up the oven books or wages sheets by the light given from the table candle-stand *(figure 32)*, that shaded the flicker from his eyes; or the "turner," who,

working after the sun had gone down, threw light upon his work by the aid of the wall sconce *(figure 31)*, which could easily be moved up or down the upright rod fixed in the wall and bench, being swung into the required position by three elbow joints. It is a marvel that, with such, to us, inadequate illumination, these ancestors of ours were able to produce the exquisite and delicate detail which was so prominent and characteristic a feature in all that came from their hands. No shoddy or scamped work seems to have been done; at least, none of it is left to us. In this matter we certainly have not improved, with all our facilities. It would almost seem that our bright illuminants only serve to spoil our eyesight.

FIGURE 29

The fire-screen *(figure 29)*, evidently a home-made article, and the tongs *(figure 33)*, go to prove that the "handy-man" existed then, and that his skill was equal to all requirements is testified in many other ways all over the old workshops.

Figure 25 shows the adaptation of material at hand which has existed, as far as any one can tell, as long as the Potteries employed female labour. It is just a piece of mirror encased in a plaster of Paris frame. You will find one in every workshop where the gentler sex are found, and ensures that the departure at "knocking off" time shall be made with hair tidy and head-gear at the right angle.

Before the days of circular heating or radiator apparatus, the two chief warming agents were the fireplace and stove-pot. *Figure 21* shows an original grate in very nearly the same state as the day when it was built, still doing duty in this particular shop; while *figure 30* gives the typical stove-pot.

The old fire-engine *(figure 39)* is another very interesting link with the past, and though made and supplied to Josiah Wedgwood in October,

FIGURE 30

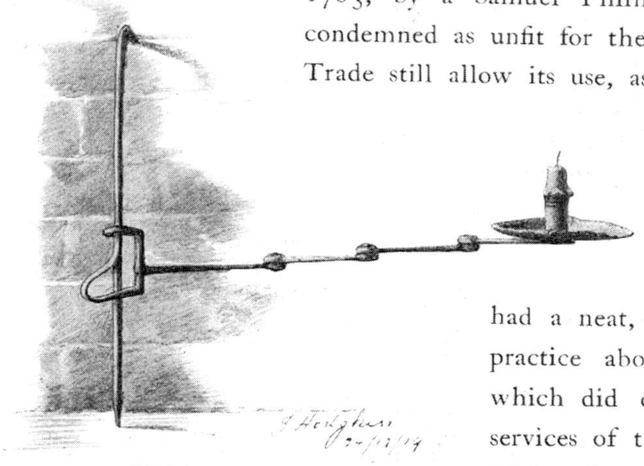

1783, by a Samuel Phillips, of London, it has never yet been condemned as unfit for the purpose it was made, for the Board of Trade still allow its use, as it is capable of throwing an efficient jet of water over the highest building on the works. The Fire Brigade was always a smart team of able-bodied men, and numbered ten members and a captain. They had a neat, serviceable uniform, and turned out at practice about four times a year, in a manner which did credit to themselves. Fortunately, the services of the fire-engine have been little required (although as late as 1915 it did all that was necessary, efficiently, until the arrival of the Stoke and Hanley Brigades), but it was always and ever ready, doing great service at fires outside the works, in the village or near neighbourhood. Of late years this old engine, with its brigade, has chiefly been used in the Fire Brigade Day processions in the Potteries district. A drawing of the engine is reproduced *(figure 39)*.

FIGURE 31

This account would not be complete without a reference to the Museum, which is on the works, and forms an important item in the tour round. Here is an opportunity of inspecting a collection of the products of Wedgwood and Etruria on the site where it was produced. It contains many of the original designs, and a wonderful collection of "trial pieces," showing the successes and failures through which this indefatigable and persistent potter passed. His energy and perseverance must have been marvellous. These trial pieces for the different "bodies," glazes, and colours are numbered in thousands, and nearly all are carefully docketed and described with reference to "mixing" book, place in oven, etc. Many of the original models are also here, and a very nearly complete assortment of the "block" moulds of the cameos, intaglios, and

FIGURE 32

portraits of eighteenth-century "illustrious moderns," as they are described in the catalogues issued by Josiah Wedgwood, F.R.S. A fine series of vases, placques, medallions and cameos in the "Jasper" ware here collected together gives the visitor an insight into the immense field which was covered by the untiring efforts to attain absolute perfection in this which was perhaps his most loved production. A good display of "Basaltes" ware shows more clearly still his keen eye for beauty of form. Three cases exhibit the development of the "Queensware" and its beauty of texture, finish and decoration. Manuscripts, deeds, indentures, letters, ledgers, oven books, and much more enlightening and interesting matter, are carefully preserved. The Museum has been equipped by the present Directors as a tribute to the past, and to form an incentive and inspiration to Ceramic posterity.

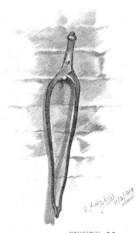

FIGURE 33

There is much more to see, and the tour of inspection will include the making and decorating processes of the ordinary table ware—dinner, dessert, tea and breakfast services, much of it hand-work, as it used to be, although a great deal of the ware is now made with machine aid. A detailed description of this is scarcely within the scope of this record.

The four drawings at the end illustrate some of the fine pieces which have always been connected with the name of Wedgwood. The central vase of *figure 41*, surmounted by Pegasus, the frieze subject being the "Apotheosis of Virgil," stands upon the Griffin pedestal and forms a noble piece of potting. One of these original vases, if not actually the first, was presented by Wedgwood to the British Museum in 1786. He says about it in a letter to Sir William Hamilton, dated June 26th, 1786: "I lamented much that I could not obtain liberty of the Merch^t to send a vase, the finest and most

FIGURE 34

perfect I have ever made, and which I have since presented to the British Museum. I enclose a rough sketch of it; it is 18 inches high, and the price 20 guineas.

FIGURE 35

Mr. Chas. Greville saw it, and wished it was in His Majesty's cabinet at Naples." In a footnote he adds: "The sketch of the vase could not be got ready for this post, but shall be sent soon:—Subject, the 'Apotheosis of Homer,' which is the companion subject upon the same vase to pair with the 'Apotheosis of Virgil.'"

On the right-hand vase the subject is "The Muses and Apollo," by Flaxman, and on the left-hand vase "The Dancing Hours," by the same eminent Royal Academician.

FIGURE 36

Five examples of Basaltes ware (which was brought to such perfection during the partnership of Wedgwood and Bentley) are shown in *figure 42*, also the "Wine" and "Water" ewers mentioned in the first invoice of Flaxman to Wedgwood in 1775.

In *figure 43*, the portrait of Thomas Bentley presides over three fine placques, viz., a "Pompeian Figure," "The Choice of Hercules," and "The Marriage of Cupid and Psyche." The latter was modelled from the Marlborough gem, which is 1¼ inches, and has been reproduced in this and various sizes up to 18 inches.

AN OLD STAIRCASE IN WAREHOUSE

FIGURE 37

CORNER OF THE "CHINA" WORKS

FIGURE 38

The last plate *(figure 44)* gives a selection of Cream Colour and Queensware, which was made in every imaginable variation for use on the table and ornamental

FIGURE 39

purposes. This ware* was produced concurrently with Jasper and Basaltes, all three creating prodigious demands upon the ingenuity of the never-failing resources of Etruria.

---

* After it had received the Royal patronage and approval of Queen Charlotte, wife of George III., and the Empress Catherine II. of Russia, who each gave commands for services to furnish the tables of their Royal Palaces, the orders flowed in to Etruria from every part of the British Isles and the Continent of Europe. The historical Green Frog service, which was made for the Empress Catherine for the Palace of La Grenouilliére, consisted of 952 pieces, having 1,244 views of English scenes painted upon it, being a record of the mansions, castles, and notable buildings in England and Scotland at that time, 1774. Unfortunately, since the looting of Petrograd during the late war, the fate of the remaining 800 pieces of this wonderful service, which had been carefully preserved in the Czarkoe Selo Palace, is unknown.

Let us now pass out through one of those doors *(figure 40)* which still preserve to us the sturdy wooden bolts, evidently constructed for the business they were called upon to do. We are back again in the twentieth century, and Etruria will still be found to hold its own in the progress which the present day demands from it, without losing the particular style that has proved at all times the valuable legacy of the illustrious Founder.

HARRY BARNARD.

Etruria, May 7th, 1920.

FIGURE 40

FIGURE 4

PART II

Joists

THE SHELTON BAR ERA

Introduction and Glossary of Terms

"As iron sharpens iron, so one man sharpens another," said Solomon in Proverbs 27 v.17. The French version is perhaps even more telling: *"Le fer aiguise le fer, le contact avec autrui affine l'esprit de l'homme."* (Iron sharpens iron, contact with another refines the spirit of man)

The stories of the great iron and steel and coal works at Etruria, first known as 'Shelton Bar', display well how workers brought out the best in each other, in comradeship, caring and dedication to the job. Their kind of work was not for the faint hearted or the weak; it was tough and dangerous, especially in the early days. Men were inspired to do great things, often to endure physical discomfort beyond the normal call of duty, to use ingenuity, imagination and tremendous expertise.

It is invidious perhaps to name names, for there are untold thousands who make up the history of this great industry; however I have used information and stories from people I have known and lived with, loved or admired, or have met seemingly by chance, and I have found it good to name them. They are representatives for the rest. The stories in the book are but a fraction of what could be told, part of the life blood of our city.

But it is necessary first of all to give a glossary of iron and steel making terms, without which some of the story would be difficult to understand. I have found this special vocabulary both interesting and at times quite amusing. A quick example of my ignorance might identify me with the many 'non-ferrous' members of the public; until very recently indeed I understood the word 'mill' to signify the building where work took place, whereas in fact it is also what the actual machinery is called - a small detail but one that others will identify with.

GLOSSARY OF IRON AND STEEL WORKS TERMS

PIGS: molten iron, cast into short 'pigs' (lumps) of cast iron, hard and brittle, and cannot be forged into any shapes.

WROUGHT IRON: made by entrapping of slag in iron, characteristicly a fibrous, spongy mass.

IRON SLAG: scum from iron making in blast furnaces; when cold and crushed became hard core for road making.

STEEL SLAG: when cold and crushed became basic slag fertiliser.

SLAG: formed by oxydation of impurities, fused waste material from iron making.

STEEL: the chief alloy of iron, the most used of metals; iron is hardened by the presence of a small amount of carbon ferro-silicon, ferro-manganese + aluminium; malleable and easy to roll when hot.

STEEL INGOTS: when cast, steel is in ingots, 5 or 6 tons, 4 or 5 ft. high, 15' square at the top and 23" at the bottom.
   These ingots are broken into:-
   A)   blooms:- 8-10 ft. long by 18" x 14" up to 24"x 17". This is cold steel before being worked.
   B)   billets: 5" x 9" square and 8-10ft long.
   C)   slabs: 42" x 8".

PUDDLING: (invented by Henry Cort, 1780s) pig iron melted and stirred, or puddled, with a long iron rod, to bring the molten iron into contact with the atmosphere and remove impurities.

HOT BLAST: heat got up in furnace from underneath; heat generated from stoves behind furnace. Could also be changed to cold blast.

SLACK: small pieces of coal with low ash content.

ANTHRACITE: highest quality coal, hard, lustrous, containing more than 90% carbon; very hot, almost smokeless.

FINERY: where pig iron was heated on a bed of charcoal (not melted), to remove impurities; then hammered whilst still hot to expel slag.

BLOWING IN: lighting of furnace.

BLOWING OUT: putting it out, which happened every five years, if the inner brickwork was badly damaged and the furnace had to be relined. This was when boulder size ore was used. When rubble size ore was used the time extended to seven years, and when sinter was used it went up to 8 or 9 years: such was the advance in iron making through ore preparation to give the furnace a longer life and thus reduce running costs.

SINTER: a mixture of secondary crushed ore, crushed coke and fluor-spar, fused together by roasting, to form a cinder.

CHAFFERY: where iron was reheated and forged to required shape, with water-powered hammers.

FETTLING: smoothing off by aggregate grit, thrown into holes in inner brick lining of furnaces, by fettlers.

AGGREGATE: a mixture of crushed materials, such as limestone, brick, cinder, slack which binds together with heat.

KALDO: a steel making rotating vessel heated by oxygen.

CONCAST: continuous casting plant for producing steel slabs, blooms and billets direct from molten metal.

SEDIMENTATION PLANT: for removing foreign bodies from the cooling water used in and around the furnaces.

TAPPING THE FURNACE: knocking out the bung of fire-clay from the furnace to allow the molten iron to run out.

COGGING MILL: a set of rolls for reducing ingots into slabs, blooms and billets; origin of word "cogging" unknown, though I had this splendid term given to me: "a neck wobbler, spine shaft, coupling drive" WOW!

OPEN HEARTH FURNACES: steel smelting furnaces using the Siemens-Martin process, (Siemens: German engineer who came to England in 1844; Martin: French engineer, licensed in 1863 to build open hearth steel process)

18" MILL: re-rolling mill producing small size British Standard steel sections and rails from billets

32" MILL: re-rolling mill producing medium to large British Standard steel sections and railway lines from blooms.

UNIVERSAL MILL: continuous re-rolling mill producing medium and large universal beams.

ROLLS: the main machinery consisting of rolls rotating, which by compression form the steel to the desired shape:

    A) breakdown - elongates billet or bloom and gives primary shape;

    B) roughing - further elongates steel and produces nearly finished state;

    C) finishing - final rolling, in most cases one pass, giving steel the required dimensions.

MANGLE: a straightening machine having vertical and horizontal pressure rollers through which the cold steel section is passed once, removing all warping and distortion resulting from normal cooling and annealing.

ANNEALING: tempering the steel by slow cooling after rolling or casting.

FLUXING: removing impurities during smelting into a formed slag (scum) on top of metal; fluxing agent limestone.

CORNER CRUSHER: primary crusher reducing boulder size ore to rubble.

RUBBLE ORE: ore the size of half a house brick.

SECONDARY CRUSHER: crusher reducing ore to pea size.

BALL MILL: a rotating drum containing loose steel balls, which reduces material to powder.

COB STEEL: during rolling at the roughing stage, sometimes a medium size section could get out of control and like a writhing snake rear up and wind itself around any adjacent structure; this was called a "cobble" and it would halt production. The offending steel had to be cut up and removed, and was called a "cob piece".

PULPIT: operator's control station: 3 main ones straddled the mill, for breakdown, roughing and finishing; auxiliary pulpits alongside the production path, for length cutting saws, cooling beds, mangle, sorting beds and loading.

A HEAT: one completed production from insertion of raw materials in furnace to the final outcome of molten metal.

A CHARGE: the materials going into the furnace.

THE BARE: central area at bottom of furnace where the molten metal settled.

THE DEMAG MILL: this is the German machine (Demag being the name of the makers), still in use today (end of 1999), which was installed in the early 1960's. The rolls and complete breakdown works were installed by German engineers, some E.E.C. Stafford and some Shelton Bar engineers, including Alf Wakefield.

JOISTS: name given to older type bars made.

UNIVERSAL BEAMS: newer form of bar used today.

Other products included tyre bars or rims for lorries and tractors; and forklift masts - a very heavy section made for the forklift firm Coventry Climax in Birmingham who couldn't roll their own.

In later years Shelton devised a means of producing double sections, which were then broken in two by a machine called 'the nutcracker'. The head roller and the design department worked this out, and it was a 'pet' project of M.D. Mr. Field. The two sections were made with a thin layer of metal between them, which when the section was completed could be separated easily by the 'nutcracker' and the edges tidied as required.

Early 1900s showing furnaces and hot air producing cylinders.

Old Etruria.

One
SHELTON BAR I

If Stoke-on-Trent had not become famous as the 'Potteries' it could easily have qualified for the name 'City of Steel', situated as it was on a site rich in minerals and coal. Iron making had taken place in a small way all over the area for 1800 years, as attested to by the late Mr. Roy Brassington in his *History of Iron Smelting in Staffordshire*. First of all charcoal was used as fuel and then in the second half of the 19th century coke took its place.

From 1760 on there was a rapid expansion both in the pottery and coal and iron industries, better roads ensuring a wider market. By 1880 coal had virtually replaced charcoal in all aspects of iron production. In the 1950s it was revealed that there were over 2,000 mine shafts in the area, some sunk before 1850. None of these was very large - perhaps over no more than ten acres and employing about ten men. The life of many mines was short, with frequent changes in ownership.

The first blast furnaces were begun at Etruria by Lord Granville in 1839, on the north east side of the Cobridge Road, for making pig iron. These were first blown in on January 4th 1841, and a memento was made of this in the shape of an elegant potter's jug, with paintings on the side depicting the new furnaces, and the inscription:

Shelton Iron Works, Staffordshire.
Erected by Earl Granville
under the management and superintendence
of William Forster,
blown in on January 4th. 1841.

Unfortunately the jug was lost during the sell-off of much of the Etruria Estate in the 1840s, however over a century later, amazingly, a director of the firm, Mr. Neville Rollason, stumbled across it in a run-down secondhand shop

The jug which commemorated the first firing in 1841

in Birmingham. We can imagine with what delight he carried it back to Etruria, and had it installed in a glass case in the boardroom.

The furnaces were extensive and still being erected in 1842. A modern 130 hp steam engine, three cupolas and the latest hot blast apparatus put Shelton Works to the fore in the district. The highest chimney rose to 160 feet. Lord Granville leased the rich coal and iron-bearing land from the Duchy of Lancaster. The coming of these iron works spelt the beginning of the end for the beautiful parkland of Etruria. At this time there was only a pathway leading from nearby Hanley down to the bottom of Cobridge Road, where stood the

Early furnaces.

GRANVILLE LEVISON GOWER,

RIGHT: Rt Hon The Earl Granville was Secretary of State for Foreign Affairs in 1854 when he initiated '*The Staffordshire Potteries Economic Permanent Building Society*' ...*to foster thrift among the employees of The Iron and Steel Co, and the inhabitants of the district*'. It became the Hanley Economic Building Society.
LEFT: His father Granville Levison Gower, the Marquis of Stafford.

The Grange colliery.

The Sneyd Colliery.

Rose and Crown pub, ready and willing to serve thirsty iron workers and miners.

The firm was called Shelton Bar Iron Co. at this time, which the workers and public soon shortened to 'Shelton Bar'. Though the name changed officially after a relatively short time (1886) it has stuck ever since with the general public. Forges and mills were erected in the 1850s and 60s, on newly leased land on the Etruria Estate, to the west of Cobridge Road. Then a 'puddling' forge and rolling mills were constructed. In 1853 Lord Granville built a railway line to enable speedier transport of the produce. Further blast furnaces were erected and by 1860 there were eight in operation.

There was a great rise in the local population as increasing numbers of people became employed at the Earl's pits and iron works. In the mid 1850s he had rows of superior cottages built for his workers at the south end of Waterloo Road, leading into Burslem from Cobridge. By now the firm was winning international awards for quality. Samuel Griffiths, a 19th century metal merchant, wrote in glowing terms of Shelton's output:

They (the iron bars etc) *are of superior quality, and may be fearlessly compared with the product of leading houses* (iron businesses) *in Staffordshire, the iron being particularly suitable for the use of railway companies, engine shops and machinists in Manchester and on the Tyne.*

In the latter part of the century the works switched to steel production, and in 1886 became the Shelton Iron, Steel and Coal Co. with Lord Granville as its first chairman. Open hearth smelting furnaces were erected and improved mills for rolling large steel sections. The Earl died in 1891, having seen his small firm grow into the largest mills in North Staffordshire. He had seen the pastoral charm of old Etruria turn into a wholly different scene, with a monstrous, fiery beauty all its own. Etruria Hall alone was spared, as we have seen, though bereft of its outer loveliness by the relentless grime.

Shortly after the 1898 Ordnance Survey Map era, Shelton installed a Simon-Carves Coking By-product Plant, which transformed the works into a modern, fully integrated iron and steel complex. The new company had become almost self contained, comprising collieries, ironstone mines, limestone and dolomite quarries, blast furnaces, steel furnaces and rolling mills - and Shelton "bars" are used all over the world to this very day at the beginning of the 21st Century.

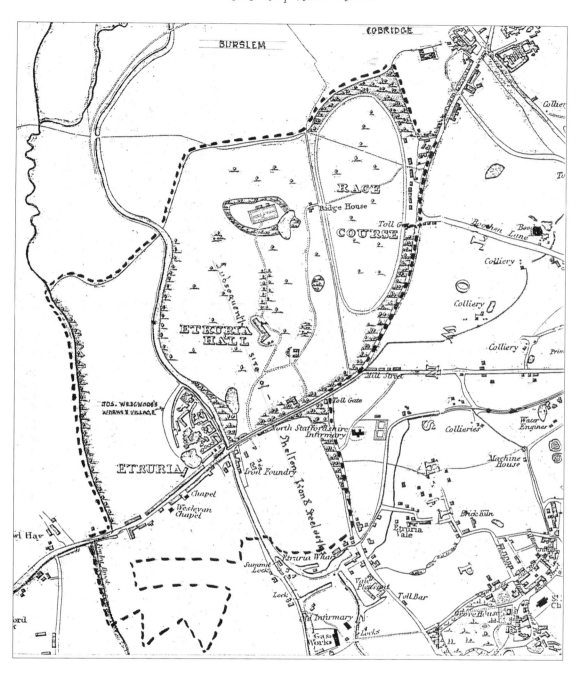

From the Hargreaves map of 1832

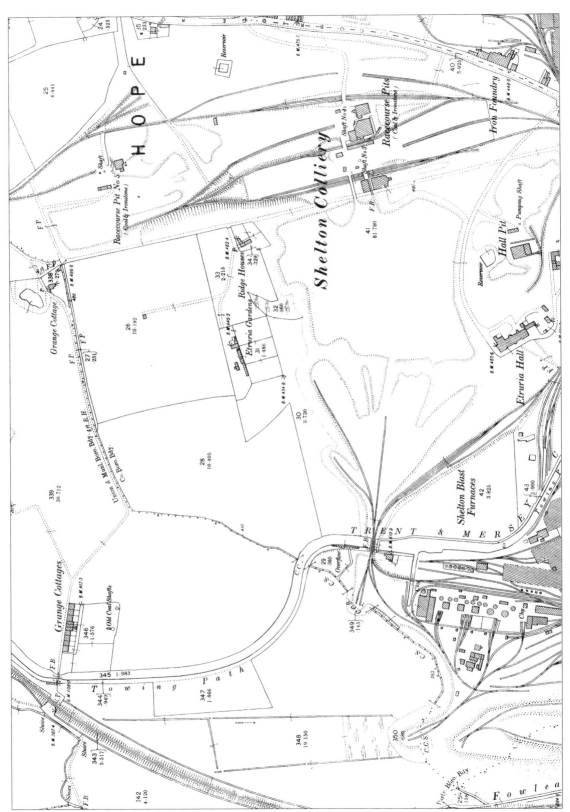

1898 Ordnance Survey

Two
RESUMÉ OF THE SHELTON BAR ERA
by the late Mr. D.H. Field M.A. C.Eng. D.L. (Managing Director)

I am pleased to have been asked to write this summary of the 20th century Shelton Steelworks, and I hope in a reasonably short space to put its whole history into clear perspective. Parts of the works are of course still in production (1998), and this gives me particular pleasure, for I used to say to the men before I retired 20 years ago, that the Demag Mill should still function well until the end of the century. This judgment was based on the level of demand for Shelton's products throughout the World, and upon the vital cost it would have meant to replace such a flexible and efficient Universal Beam Mill. There is not long to go now before the millenium!

North Staffordshire has been a major iron making area since the 17th century owing to the presence of iron ore and coal, as well as water. In the early days iron producing was a slow and laborious business, using the puddling process (pig iron reheated until molten, oxidising agent added, then stirred manually). In the early part of the 19th century the blast furnace was coming into use as the major producer of iron, but still based on charcoal and then coal/coke use. The enormous improvement came with the use of a blast of air, later heated, at the bottom of the furnace. Since that time there have been many and considerable further improvements, but the blast furnace remains the major producer of iron.

In the late 1830s, as we have seen, Earl Granville, who owned several collieries, began his ironworks on the North (Hanley) side of Cobridge Road, the first blast furnace being blown in 1841. The iron was further refined in puddling furnaces, of which, by 1873, there were 97. There were also small rod and bar mills, (hence the famous name Shelton Bar Iron Co.) as well as plate and othe section mills. It was a wise decision to build the works in this position, not only because of the abundance of raw materials available here, but also because it was near to the canal, without which in those days transport costs would have been prohibitive. In addition Shelton was right on the spot for the market of the industrial Midlands.

IRON AND STEEL MAKING IN 1892
We have a very accurate and thorough Consultant's Report on the operation of the collieries and iron and steel works at this time. It runs into 75 pages, but sadly the plans and maps are missing, which is so often the case with old documents. The blast furnace plant had been constructed in the position it occupied at Etruria until its closure in 1978. On this site there were six furnaces, hence the more recent numbers of the furnaces 1, 4 and 6. Horses were used to haul slag and iron ladles, as noted elsewhere, because of the very restricted access, a point which caused trouble always, as only small locomotives could be used later. The furnaces were charged with ore and coal, the latter giving considerable trouble owing to the fouling of the mains with tar. These required regular cleaning which was both a difficult and very unpleasant job. The iron from the furnaces was run into pigs (pig-beds), which were in the open and of which there is more information in another chapter.

The Consultant's Report is severely critical of the use of coal in the blast furnaces and it noted also that this commodity was passed to the furnaces at far too low a cost, thereby hiding many deficiencies in the furnace costs. There was criticism as well in that the most senior manager in the collieries rarely, if ever, went underground!

With the installation of Compound Underjet Coke Ovens soon after this period the problems of coal in the blast furnaces ceased. Shelton won many awards for its products, in Paris, Melbourne and other major exhibitions, both in the early days and in later years too.

At this time there were 28 puddling furnaces and a series of small mills on the Shelton side of the works, 20" general purpose, 22" plate, 22" bar, 12" mill, 10" mill and 9" guided mill. (These will mean something to those connected with the industry). On the Etruria site there was a new Open Hearth Furnace plant, consisting of two furnaces, with a further two under construction. These produced 11 charges per week. Near these furnaces was a new 32" mill. Both of these plants were in continuous production until closed in 1963, when the new Steel Plant and Demag Mill took over.

At the time of the Report, the works was going through one of its periodic difficult phases with a great recession in the industry. There is a letter in existence from Gladstone, who was Prime Minister at that period, to the Earl saying, "*I hear sorry news about the state of the iron trade.*" History repeats itself!

ADVANCEMENT OVER THE EARLY PART OF THE 20TH CENTURY

Iron and steel works being highly capital intensive usually result in utilisation of any new plant to the ultimate, and then, when other firms have passed you by, a giant step forward is taken to be ahead of everyone else! The skill is in deciding when the step should be taken! This depends on the existing profitability of the plant, the likelihood of technical advances and the probable market for one's products. It was the use of this foresight which enabled Shelton to outlast all other iron and steel works in North Staffordshire. After such large technical advances there would follow a period of consolidation with minor improvements.

A bridge was built over the canal, and this enabled ore to be brought from the stocking ground to some new high level bunkers, for charging the furnaces. This charging was done via the "vertical and horizontal hoist arrangement", unique to Shelton in the World. The reason for this was (once more) shortage of space, and the machine was invented and made by Shelton expertise! Materials for the furnaces were lifted partly vertically and partly horizontally.

The steel plant was modernised just before the 1939-45 war, and though undergoing a minor bombing raid, served the Country well during the conflict. In particular, sections were produced and rolled in high grade steel for armaments and Bailey bridges. Early in the 1940s Their Majesties King George V and Queen Elizabeth visited the works, and they were shown round by Managing Director, Mr Neville Rollason.

During this period there were 4,500 people employed on the steelworks and a very large number in the five collieries. In 1937 there was a great disaster at Holditch Colliery, which has been well documented in another place. Suffice to say that the Managing Director at the time, Mr. John Cocks, who led the rescue team, was himself killed.

The 1930s saw the problems of recession in the industry and Shelton was not spared. However, this is where the flexibility of a small plant paid dividends. With three blast

A view of the works by Alf Wakefield.

furnaces it was possible to produce varying grades of iron (Shelton still sold iron to some customers direct), and the mills were often changed for rolling 20 tons as against a normal rolling of about 750 tons. In this manner the firm remained in business until the upturn came. The attitude of helping the work force wherever possible produced a wonderful team spirit which was always evident at Shelton. Management and the workforce trusted each other completely, and everything possible was done to provide continuous employment: this policy was handsomely repaid by the total co-operation of the workers.

THE JOHN SUMMERS ERA

In 1919, John Summers & Sons from Shotton, Deeside, purchased the entire works at Shelton. This was to secure their supply of coal and pig iron, as at the time they did not have their own blast furnaces. It is interesting to note that when Summers did install their own blast furnace plant several key workers from Shelton were recruited to get this Shotton plant running! The relationship with Summers lasted for exactly 50 years when, after the second nationalisation, Shelton was transferred to the Scottish and East Moors Group of the British Steel Corporation. It had been a very happy and mutually beneficial relationship and during this entire period a Summers or a Rollason was always Chairman at Shelton.

This 50 year relationship is recorded for posterity in the form of a magnificent Wedgwood bowl with views of the old works and the new. The manufacture of the bowls by Wedgwood completed the link with that firm on this famous Etruria site, and although many people on the steelworks must have had relatives at Wedgwoods, the secret of the ware being made was never released ahead of time. The 50 year relationship was celebrated at a dinner held at Trentham Gardens, which was attended by a large number of Shelton employees with long service, Sir Richard Summers and other directors. A bowl was presented to Sir Richard

to be retained at the Shotton Works, and bowls were presented to Sir Richard personally, Mr. Melvin Rollason and Mr. Gray, all of whom performed wonderful work for Shelton. In addition there were 4 members of staff, whose service of over 50 years spanned the entire time the firms were united, and they were each presented with a suitably inscribed plate. The Shelton copy of the bowl is in the City Museum at Hanley.

Mr Neville Rollason, who lived at Tittensor (and later during the war at Peplow), was Director of Shelton from 1936 until the early 1940s, when he went as MD to Shotton; at which time his elder brother, Mr Melvin Rollason, took over at Shelton. Neville Rollason was one of the most outstanding men in the steel industry and the developments and success of John Summers were very largely due to his foresight and flair for knowing the right thing to do and when to do it! With Sir Richard Summers' business acumen and banking connections and Mr. Reith Gray's brilliance at running in a new plant, virtually by sitting on the job, they made a great team which could not be matched anywhere in the industry. This worked out to Shelton's great advantage as will be noted later.

At the time, Shelton's Construction Department had expanded considerably, to help with developments at Shotton and when these were completed they went into the open market: they secured orders for three hospitals in Australia and two large buildings in Hong Kong. One of these, the Chartered Bank in St George''s Square, was the tallest in the colony at the time! However, difficult times lay ahead.

During the boom in steel making which occurred after the Second World War, the Shelton plant, though very old, was operating effectively and profitably. However, in the late 1950s it was obvious that it could not remain competitive indefinitely, particularly with the advent of Universal Beams and Columns, which require a special type of rolling mill. The blast furnaces were very old and small, though flexible. It was a difficult plant to manage as

there was no gas holder and one furnace only had a single bell type mechanism for charging. The open hearth plant was rapidly being superceded by the L.D. Process, where pure oxygen was blown in the top of a converter, producing steel in about a tenth of the time. This was an invention of Sir Henry Bessemer in England in the 19th century, which had not been proceeded with here because, being air-blown at the time (pure oxygen being impossible to produce), there was an entrapment of nitrogen in the steel, with poor results.

After a long discussion with Mr Neville Rollason, the Blast Furnace manager, Mr. Davis chose to have a sinter plant rather than a new furnace. This proved to be absolutely the correct decision as it helped to produce a better charge, which benefited all three furnaces. This plant was installed at the latter end of the 1950s.

Sinter plant, left,
and below, later coke ovens.

The problems for the rest of the plant were entirely different. Shelton could not justify building a plant with a greatly increased output as our market research showed that there would not be the demand under normal circumstances: it is a fatal move to put in a plant to deal with peaks in demand, because it has to operate at less than full output for most of its life, with resultant problems of cost. The political decision to build Llanwern (South Wales) and

Ravenscraig (Scotland) was a prime example of this.

To install a conventional type of plant for the tonnage required would not have been viable. Many people in Summers' position would have closed down and transferred the work to Shotton. However, our Principals did not take this view. Shelton had served them well for many years and they felt a special responsibility towards the 3,800 people and their families who were dependent on the works. Many of them had given a lifetime of service to Shelton!

THE MODERN WORKS

In 1959 a very bold and imaginative decision was taken to install a Kaldo pneumatic steel-making furnace, a continuous casting plant and a Universal Beam and Section Mill. This was a completely revolutionary type of plant which did not exist anywhere in the World at the time. The Kaldo process was selected rather than the more usual L.D. furnace, because there was better control of temperature - a vital point with continuous casting - it used a higher proportion of scrap iron which was readily available, and there was greater control over analysis of the steel in the medium carbon range for sections.

Instead of using the traditional ingot and soaking pits together with a heavy break-down mill, it was decided to use continuous casting, whereby a bloom of the correct size was produced in water-cooled moulds; this could then be reheated in a push type furnace and then pass straight through the 3 stands in the rolling mill without further heating. The rolling mill had interchangeable housings which could be lifted out by a giant 200 ton crane and either Universal Beams or normal sections could be rolled.

The decision to use continuous casting was a bold one, and with a much higher yield the rewards to be gained were very great. We needed to cast sizes up to 24" x 17", which had never been cast in the World previously. There were many smaller sizes as well to suit the many sections which were rolled. Shelton was the first steelworks in the entire World to take this route and to have its whole output through continuous casting.

Naturally the problems in commissioning such a revolutionary plant were enormous and without the guiding hand of Mr Reith Gray, as well as his calming influence, I am not sure what would have happened. Panic situations seemed to occur daily at times! I personally owe a considerable debt to this remarkable man of enormous experience and expertise. Being a "first" in anything is never easy as there is no-one to turn to for help and advice.

These were not the only 'firsts' that Shelton notched up. Following the Universal Beam Mill was the unique Finishing Department, completely designed by Shelton people. Orders were sorted immediately after rolling on the cooling banks and then passed through the roller straightener as complete orders. In this way they were able to be stacked and dispatched within 4 hours of rolling, instead of the normal 5 or 6 days! This feat was not believed possible by most people until they visited the works, when they realised that with the small space available it had to be done. This method saved at least 3 or 4 days of finished materials having to be kept in stock.

The patent stacker for beams and channels was designed by the Foreman Engineer in the mill whose father had been foreman before him. Once when I was walking back through the mill area during construction I saw this man, Graham Rasbridge, looking very worried, so I stopped and asked him what the problem was. He replied, *"It's these blessed contractors: they simply will not get a move on!"*

I replied that he shouldn't worry too much as Rome wasn't built in a day!

The quick rejoinder was, *"No, Sir, but I wasn't foreman on that job!"* This epitomised the attitude and enthusiasm of the Shelton people absolutely (and the humour too).

Everyone in the World, including the Japanese, were interested in what we were doing. No-one else had complete reliance on continuous casting and such a revolutionary mill and finishing end. We had visitors from everywhere, and if things went wrong somewhere it was certainly embarrassing, as there was no hiding things when the plant was standing idle!

The estimated cost of this tremendous development was £18.5 million, and it was essential that we should not be overspent, as most other steel works carrying out major developments were - which gave them a millstone of capital cost around their necks from which they could never recover. The worst example of this was at Llanwern, where the estimate was nearly doubled! Our development cost was by far the greatest amount of money that had ever been spent in this area by one firm, but, after continuing to concrete through the coldest winter this century - the temperature never rose above freezing for 76 consecutive days and nights - we were only £500,000 overspent! This remarkable achievement was attained by really "getting the message down" to the lowest possible level; namely that any extra cost involving more than £100 had to receive approval from the Head of the Section, (in my own case Structural and Civil Work), before it could proceed. This had always been Shelton's method -"look after the small things and the rest will fall into place."

Hence we were able to achieve the work within the costs set for it (later in the book are some details given to me by Works Electrical Design Engineer, Mr. Les Hall, who also talked of the need to keep within the 'budget'. When I mentioned this to Mr. Field, he smiled wryly, saying that it always seemed to him that Les's recommendations as regards the electrical equipment were meant for a 'Rolls Royce' type works! Only the best was good enough for Shelton in the eyes of devoted Les!)

Sadly the Kaldo was an interminable problem through its lining costs (see note below*), and we were unable to resolve this however we tried. Instead of getting 120 charges (loads) per lining we were lucky to achieve 80, often a good deal less. I remember many occasions when we were down to one Kaldo, and when that failed we were without steel-making. This problem could not have been foreseen as the only Kaldo in operaton before our own was a 15 ton model at Domnarvet in Sweden, where all was well. Later they put in a larger model and then had exactly the same problem.

About now the spectre of nationalisation was looming up again and it was pretty obvious that the Government meant business this time - they were going to "scramble everything up" so that the procedure could not be reversed. Shelton's own plan was to abandon the blast furnace route and install one or two Electric Arc Furnaces - we lived in a scrap arising area (i.e. plenty of scrap was always available), and it was an ideal steel-making method to serve continuous casting machines. The plan to achieve this was unacceptable through the normal management channels, and it was suggested that the best course for Shelton was to instigate an 'Action Committee' to enable access to MPs and other senior people in the steel industry. [If their immediate superior at divisional level, a Mr. Morley - no relation to me I hasten to add - turned down the scheme, they would have had no right of appeal to a higher level]. Thus the Action Committee came into being and later played an important and impressive role in the struggle for the survival of the works, as recorded elsewhere.

*Some interesting information on this came from another source: Bricks for the lining of the Kaldo came in immensely heavy square metre containers, made from superior quality wood, in order to contain their loads from Austria. The bricks were black and very dense and shaped to fit exactly into the various sections of the lining. They were extremely expensive, as can be gathered from these details. Incidentally the wooden containers were then discarded, and as was the practice of the Shelton firm, workers were allowed to take such materials for their own use. The supplier of this information actually constructed for himself a superior garden shed from some of this very wood!

Derailed steel ladle, early 1900s.

Suffice to say, when Lord Beswick conducted his review of the industry, Shelton was the only works to have BSC's plans reversed! We actually went to Japan to look at electric arc furnaces and reached a licensing agreement with one maker, only to have this squashed when the international recession occurred in steelmaking in 1977.

And so, after 137 years of iron and steel making on the Shelton site, the end came in 1978 with the closure of the blast furnaces, the steel plant and the continuous casting machines. It was the end of an era for many families who had known no other way of life. The last few months before I took early retirement were the worst that I had ever experienced. After working for Summers and the Shelton people, we found it a different world. Going round the plant was traumatic. Men would say to me,*"We hear they want to close this or that down, but we know as long as we see you walking around it will be alright!"* How could you answer that one? Shelton was a wonderful, happy place of work for so many families, and the relationship with management could hardly have been improved upon. The senior managers "walked the works" daily and never passed anyone without a brief word. It was a wonderful way to get information across as whoever was told anything would pass it on as a matter of course. There was complete trust and I can remember instances of a major breakdown, when men as well as managers would just get stuck into the repair job without even asking what extra they would be receiving. When other firms heard of this they did not believe it, but Shelton men knew that they would not be let down, and would receive just and fair rewards.

Even with orders much went on trust, and the BSC found this difficult to accept or believe. Two instances spring to mind:

1. We were sole supplier to a firm called British Guide Rails, which made guide rails for lift shafts. They were a difficult section to roll and had to be very accurate as they were set up in batches of six

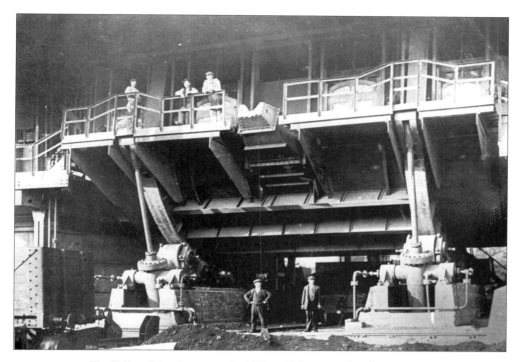

The Talbot tilting furnace early 1920s which operated until the 1960s.

on a machining table. When the B.S.C. officials came to check through our ordering system they could find no trace of the B.G.R. orders - this was hardly surprising because there really weren't any! The driver would take a load over by road and when he came back he would report that they were a bit short of a particular size (there were three in total), and so he would take some over the next day. They were invoiced at the end of the month and they were never late in paying, so what more could one ask? But the B.S.C. asked plenty!

2. All the steelworks were in the British Export Association, except Shelton, where we conducted our own affairs! Prices were agreed upon between makers and orders were apportioned out. They were pretty sure that Shelton were undercutting the price as we always had good orders. They really could not wait to make us reveal our books! What a surprise they got when they found that we were receiving prices far in excess of those achieved by themselves! It was all done by customer relations: we had an export agent in Birmingham and often he would ring our General Manager, Mr. Herbert, and ask if we would like a rolling, i.e. an order, of a certain section and tonnage at such and such a price. All we had to do was check the situation regarding the rolls and when we could mount them on the mill, and an answer was available in 1 or 2 hours. Nobody could give better service than that!

Shelton really was a unique place, and I for one am thankful that I was able to spend the 25 happiest years of my industrial life there. Sadly it can never be the same again. I remember when I first came to the firm in 1953, the first long service award was given after 50 years, and there were masses of recipients as such men had joined probably at 12 or 13 years of age! They received a gold half-hunter pocket watch from Astbury's in Bond Street - quite something to be proud of! Men would tell me that they had two, three or four gold watches in their family for instance! Generations of men and boys, yes, and ladies too, have served the firm loyally all their working lives.

Beginning the building of the Bunker Bridge over the Trent and Mersey canal, c.1920s.

The bridge being built over the canal c.1920s. 'Bunker Bridge' girders shown in position.
Note cows in the background in Grange fields.

Shelton blast furnaces and pig beds in 1890.

Nos 1, 4 & 6 blast furnaces 1978. The four top projections are the 'candles' of No. 1.

The coke ovens.

Early 1900s. Left background, power station cooling towers. Left foreground, bricks for building culverts from the canal to the turbo-blower house for cooling condensers. In background 32" rolling mill and melting shop.

Three
SHELTON BAR II

Some of this chapter is quite technical, much of it from the electrical point of view. However, ex-steelworkers will surely follow it and the account is well seasoned with tit-bits of general information. It shows the dedication of the man who supplied it, namely the late Mr. Leslie Hall, Electrical Engineer and Designer to Shelton Bar, who desperately wanted the story of Shelton Bar recorded for posterity. He, like many of us, was overjoyed by the transformation of the Garden Festival site.

I would also like to apologise at this point to the ex-miners at Shelton for the dirth of information about their work. The fact is that I never came into contact with any of them during my research on the Garden Festival site.

The first coke 40 ovens at Shelton were erected in 1905, and a further 15 in 1907. Reconstruction in 1913-14 brought an entirely new battery of 36 ovens of the latest type. By 1952 there were 76 in operation The company had been acquired by John Summers and Sons of Shotton near Chester in 1919.

During the First World War Shelton worked flat out to meet wartime demands, just as it did 25 years later when World War Two meant another massive increase in demand for iron and steel. At the outbreak of war in 1939 the Shelton Company consisted of:

A) 5 coal mines - Deep Pit Hanley, Silverdale, Holditch (Chesterton), Florence (Longton) and Racecourse (Cobridge) - producing 2 million tons of coal per annum.

B) 3 blast furnaces, No. 1, 4, and 6 (No.1 was large and 4 and 6 smaller) producing 347,000 tons of pig iron per annum. This was the production from two furnaces as the other would be subject to relining or maintenance. There were occasions however when all three were in production at the same time, and then the output would be 600,000 tons. This did not happen often as after seven years working a furnace <u>had</u> to have a complete re-line. In earlier days the work took about 12 months, but by the 1950s this was reduced to 12-13 weeks! With routine maintenance 2 furnaces working was ideal and supplied the needs of Shelton, John Summers Shotton, Round Oak Steelworks Darlaston and other small Midland works.

C) 5 open hearth furnaces, A, F, G, H, and J, all of 80 ton capacity, and gas fired (coal gas). The J. Furnace was of the Talbot type, which was mechanically tilted for tapping. There were always 4 furnaces in production continuously, with one being re-lined. 200,000 tons of steel were produced annually.

D) Coke ovens: 1, 2, and 4 batteries, each comprising 36 ovens. Normal production was from 2 working batteries, mainly 1 and 4, with 2 as standby. There were two subsidiary companies associated with the coking plant: the New Acid Company and Staffordshire Chemical Company, both situated at the north of Longport Station alongside the canal. Here liquid chemicals like benzine, naptha, creosote, tar and sulphuric acid etc. were refined for sale.

E) 32" steel rolling mill at Etruria, comprising (a) a cogging mill, reducing by rolling a 5 ton ingot to blooms and billets; (b) a combined breakdown, roughing and finishing mill, producing heavy and medium size rolled steel joists, channels, angles, flat bottom and bullnosed railway lines from blooms.

F) 18" rolling mill at Shelton, producing light gauge rolled steel joists, angles and small gauge rails used in coal mines, from billets.

The whole complex - coal, coke, iron and steel (including rolling mills) employed 6,000 personnel.

In 1939 the Directors of Shelton Iron, Steel and Coal Company Ltd were Mr Richard F. Summers - Chairman, Mr Neville H. Rollason - Managing Director, Mr Melvyn Rollason - Resident at Shelton, Mr A.A. Batt - Company Secretary, Mr W.H. Lake - Chief Engineer, Mr H.A. Morley - Works Manager, Mr John Walker (collieries) based at Etruria, and Professor Granville Poole (collieries) non-resident. Some of these retired between 1939 and 1945.

WARTIME 1939-45.

During the Second World War Shelton played its part in meeting massive military demands for steel, thus certain developments were necessary to keep abreast with production requirements. In 1941 a 1,000 HP elecrical Ward Leonard Drive (or 'motor' to civilians) was installed to power the cogging rolls in the 32" mill. This had been powered originally from the 1,000 HP steam engine which drove all the rolls in the 32" mill. When installed the new drive gave greater rolling flexibility to the mill as now cogging rolling of ingots could take place at the same time as breakdown, roughing and finishing of steel products. Also in 1941 there was an extension of the Power Station and the installation of a 3MV BTH alternator and associated 5.5KV HT switch gear and steel tank rectifiers supplied from a 1,000KVA transformer.

1942 saw the installation of a twin strand pig casting machine using a conveyor mould system to produce pigs from teemed (ie. poured) molten iron. This did away with the old, uneconomic, work-intensive method of making pig iron in sand formed pig beds laid out in front of each furnace. Also in 1942 a hot metal mixer and associated building, and overhead ladle crane with a 40 ton capacity, were installed. This provided an 'on tap' hot metal supply to the melting shop, eliminating the need to use cold pig iron, and reducing smelting time in the open hearth furnaces.

In 1943 another addition to the Power Station was the installation of 2 Siemens IMV alternators, purchased secondhand from Plymouth Corporation. And in 1944 a new steam raising boiler plant was installed, which included 3 international pulverised fuel boilers, complete with convectors, automatic coal crushers and feeders. A 4th Simon Carves boiler was added 12 months later.

In 1945 came the installation of a "Ross" ore cone crusher, complete with vertical wagon hoist off-loading. This was situated down on the Grange, and had its own electrical sub-station, transformers and control equipment. It reduced the ore from boulder size to rubble - the size of half a house brick, which when fed into the blast furnace considerably reduced the smelting time, and saved wear and tear on the furnace lining, thus extending the time of the working life of the furnace from the 'blowing in' to 'damping down'.

During the early war years several attempts were made to bomb the works, but only one bomb landed within the works perimeter and this did little material damage, landing on a concrete area at the rear of the 32" mill reheating furnace. Had the bomb landed 50 feet further north it would have gone into the reheating furnace! When you consider that bombs landed in the Hall Fields between the works and Etruria Road , and in various parts of the area all around, with some loss of life unfortunately, Shelton Company was lucky to remain almost unscathed. The whole works carried on to supply all the Ministry of Defence demands, particularly producing shell steel ingots, which were rolled into billets in the 32" mill, before dispatch to munitions works throughout the Midlands.

A poignant letter from *The Way We Were* no. 33, 1997, is of interest here:

> Sir, -- With reference to your article in the December issue under the headline "Heroes of the gasworks blaze". One sentence which caught my eye was *"In the event, the vast steelworks escaped virtually unscathed."* I would like to bring to your attention the fact that on September 5th 1940, Shelton Bar had a direct hit in which one man was killed. His name was Mr. Arthur Bloor, my father, who was 43. He was a boiler attendant and in my eyes, and the eyes of my family, he was a real unsung hero. Unknown to many, he had been asked by the management of Shelton Bar to stay behind after the air raid warning had sounded to isolate four boiler units situated at different points on the plant.
>
> To my mind, the Shelton Bar management did not give him the recognition he deserved. All they would say was that it was an act of God. My mother received not a penny or a letter of thanks in recognition of what my father did for the company. My mother was left to bring up a family of four children, three of them of school age, on a widow's pension.
>
> I am now 67 but have lived with that dreadful night all my life. I still think of my father as one of the many unsung heroes.
>
> G.W. Bloor, a proud son, Bentilee.

If this refers to the incident above it would seem that a serious injustice was done, perhaps inadvertently. It adds to the saga of Shelton Bar, and hopefully belatedly redresses the issue a little!

NOTE ON STEAM USE

Prior to the advent of electricity Shelton relied on steam for its prime 'mover'. Therefore the works was literally strewn with boilers producing steam. With the progression of electricity the individual fired boilers were eliminated, and when the International Boilers [plus Simon Carves] went into operation they disappeared completely. However the waste boilers were retained in service, as steam was still required for certain applications. Re-heating furnace and heat soaking pits were required to reheat blooms, billets and ingots prior to rolling, and these created surplus waste heat; thus a boiler was placed adjacent to the furnace - in the case of the 32" mill bloom reheating furnace, at the rear - and the waste heat was blown in to boil the water and produce steam. This is yet another example of 'NOTHING BEING WASTED AT SHELTON'.

LIGHTING

With the end of the War Shelton realised that there would be an enormous demand for their products, particularly in the bomb damaged cities throughout the land. To meet this they set out on a programme to modernise and replace worn equipment.

During 1946-7 mercury high bay lighting was installed in every building through the whole of the Shelton and Etruria works, and also outside lighting. Until that time the lighting had been extremely primitive and outside just did not exist! Shelton workers took their bearings during the hours of darkness from office lighting, furnace illumination, red hot bars etc. All walls, door posts and column foundations were white-washed frequently at the base, to help them find their way around. Within the main buildings and finishing sheds, lights (no more than absolutely necessary) did exist, mounted no higher than 15 feet where essential work was carried out: ie. for presses, mangles and straightening machines.

There was a 'form' of lighting - suspended from the understructure of each overhead crane there were 4 boxes containing six 1,000 watt lamps: thus, as the crane moved the ground below was illuminated for the ground slinger to work. But, no crane - no light! (The compilers of the booklet *150 Years of Shelton Works* could not have walked the works at night in the 1930s, for the picture shown on page 17 called "the works at night 1924" was taken in fact in 1950! The lighting shown is high bay mercury, the outside lighting installed in 1946-7. Also the aluminium painted chimney in the centre, very prominent in the picture, was erected in 1950 as part of the new oil firing installation!)

NATIONALISATION

1947 saw a major change in structure for Shelton Iron, Steel and Coal Company, when the nationalisation of the coal industry removed Hanley Deep Pit, Siverdale, Florence and Holditch Collieries (the Racecourse pit closed in 1942 because of flooding) from the company. The loss of the collieries had no effect on the iron and steel production, but did lead to the formation of a new company, which was to make Shelton a worldwide name within the building construction industry.

At the 'Top Works' (the Shelton end of the works) there was a large two-bay building which housed 4 overhead cranes, known as the Boiler Shop. In this building iron and steel fabrications were manufactured for collieries - pit cages, pit tubs, conveyor structures etc - and for the iron and steel works - furnace doors, charging boxes, furnace steel frame structures, tapping chutes etc. About a thousand men were employed here and when the N.C.B. (National Coal Board) stated that they intended to build their own boilershop elsewhere in the district it meant a 50% loss of work to the Shelton boilershop, with employment redundancies. Rather than face this the Shelton Company decided to branch out into the construction industry, in the name of the Shelton Construction Company.

During 1950-51 a third bay was erected on the Hanley side of the boilershop, this name then being dropped and the section being known from then on as the "Construction Department". The new bay was larger than the 1 and 2 bays and housed one 5 ton and two 15 ton overhead cranes. Number 1 bay, which was shorter than the no.2 bay, was extended in length, and large design and drawing offices were built on waste land between the department and Cobridge Road. At the Century Street end of the construction building a large steel stocking ground was put down complete with Goliath crane. Inside the building the latest construction manufacturing equipment was installed - Boulton and Paul fully automated saw and drill line, and on line and off welders, including radial operating welders for chimneys etc. (on line = fixed on production line, and off line = moveable, for plugging in where needed)

A sales office was opened in Birmingham, and thus the Shelton Construction Company was born, employing 350 men, producing constructional steelwork for buildings, bridges, etc., designed at Shelton, and using steel produced in Shelton's 18" and 32" mills. This company ran successfully for 25 years until 1976, when the British Steel Corporation closed it down and hived it off to the private sector in Warrington! To this day buildings worldwide are standing which were designed and constructed at Shelton. (I noted with interest in a newspaper article of 1995 how a technician from our own New Vic Theatre, while adapting staging for a production of *Nice Girl* at a French theatre on the outskirts of Paris, spotted the mark of 'British Steel Shelton' on the buildings framework. It warmed my heart!). When you travel by road to Colwyn Bay and Llandudno on the A55 you go under and over bridges on the St. Asaph bypass-Rhyl flyover all designed and constructed at Shelton. The constructional department buildings are still in existence, the design offices occupied by Moorland Electronics and the 3-bay building by Brown McFarlane Steel Stockists.

One pleasing aspect of the collieries takeover was that the N.C.B. decided not to manufacture colliery underground arches, which became a profitable part of the 18" mill's work, using steel produced and sited alongside the mill.

REGENERATION

Shelton Bar had survived two world wars and the depression years between. The time had now come to review the plant, most of which was over 40 years old and in need of replacement. Thus for the next decade vast sums of money were spent in a regeneration and modernisation programme. The first major installation was the ore stocking ground on the west side of the ore crusher, complete with Goliath crane, wagon tippler and full length tripper type off-loading conveyor. The oil firing of the 5 steel furnaces quickly followed, eliminating the gas producing plant, which stetched the full length of the west side of the melting shop. The steel furnace doors were electrified, doing away with the steam operated opening and shutting mechanics. Waste heat and stove blowing fans, which were steam powered, had electrically operated motor fans fitted throughout the mills and the blast furnaces.

The work included the refurbishing and replacing of all electrical control equipment which was over 40 years old, on all overhead cranes, furnace chargers, coking plant hopper loaders, coke pushers etc throughout the Shelton works; and also the replacement of stranded wire electrical conductors with copper wheel pick-ups, up-to-date solid copper conductors, insulator supported, and copper insert trolley boom pick-ups.

The basic slag works had fully automated conveyor and bag loading systems installed. A fully automated coal blending plant went into action at the coking plant, under newly constructed concrete storage bunkers (5 in all, one for Welsh slack and four for other, local, slacks, all fed automatically onto a conveyor bed beneath, in correct amounts of each, and mixed to produce the really good grades of coke required), and loading conveyors connecting the existing wagon tippler for incoming materials. When this system was installed the control desk was one of the first in the Country to have an illuminated mimic flow panel included! Manufactured by Allen West and Co, Brighton, it was displayed at the Electrical Exhibition at Earl"s Court, London, where it attracted much attention, prior to shipment to Shelton.

A rolling lathe powered by a 50 HP electric motor was installed in the 32" mill roll lathe shop. This cost Shelton nothing other than payment for installation, and provides an interesting story: When World War II ended the British Government decided to scrap German iron and steel works, but stated that any equipment not bomb damaged should be handed over to British steelmakers. This was one such machine, brand new, which had not yet been installed! It was a lovely piece of machinery and far better than anything they had at Shelton. It was installed in the 32" mill roll lathe shop in 1949, and worked every day until 1964, when the 32" mill closed!

This next bit of information gives cause for thought indeed! After the German iron and steel industry was scrapped international aid was poured into Germany. Thus, by the mid-1950s they had new iron and steel works, production of which OUTSTRIPPED BRITISH WORKS! They captured the world markets and their economy left ours standing! The Germans were up and going with new works, whilst Shelton had to wait until 1964 to replace plant over 50 years old! (My father said at the time that steel ingots were being exported to Germany, where they were made into various products, and returned to England for sale, stamped with a German mark!) We might have won the war, but we certainly lost the peace! How history repeats itself! Wasn't it Bismarck who first said that of England during the 19th. Century?

To continue the improvements, electrically operated swing-in compressed air pug rams were installed on all 3 blast furnace tap holes and the manual gas retort feeds on all coke ovens were removed and replaced by automatic electrical systems. The power station was extended to receive a 2.2MV alternator, the turbine of which was powered by blast furnace gas (with oil alternative). This was the first alternator in the world to use blast furnace gas to drive the turbine. It was the prototype unit manufactured by Richard Westgarth, and Shelton agreed to its installation to prove that it was a satisfactory invention - which it was! During the miners' strike of the 1970s this alternator played a valuable role in keeping the works supplied with electricity as the turbine did not require steam (coal produced) to drive.

A new charger was installed at the melting shop replacing the south unit which was 30 years old. At the 18" mill electrically operated floor-lifting equipment was put in on the north side of the rolling stands. All machines in the machine shop, (lathes, shapers, millers' drill etc) were fitted with individual motor drives.

An ore preparation and sinter plant was installed on the canal side of the ore stocking ground, to further reduce the iron smelting times in the blast furnaces. Secondary crushing of the rubble ore made it pea size and this was mixed with crushed coke in powder form and fluor spar, and all this was fed onto a 300 x 12ft heating conveyor belt made of linked iron fire bars. At the head of the conveyor the mix was spread evenly some two inches thick and heated with a white hot gas (forced heat) flame, until it became a red hot mass of sinter - in other words a 'sinter mass'. The conveyor moved slowly (so slowly that the movement was just visible to the naked eye) through its 100ft. length. (Peter Cheeseman describes this vividly in his notes on the show *Fight for Shelton Bar*)

As the sinter mass left the heated area it had sufficient heat to fully cook, and during its travel would cool until at the end of the 300ft. it would drop off the conveyor, to fall into waiting wagons beneath to go on to the blast furnace bunkers.

A water softening plant was installed to feed the boiler plant. A pumphouse was erected on Fowlea Brook to provide additional water for the blast furnaces, the pipework running through a pit-like tunnel (of which more in another chapter), through a large slag heap. A sedimentation plant was built to clean the used water prior to return to the Fowlea Brook.

MORE POWER

33KV and 11KV sub-stations were erected to receive electrical supplies from the Midlands Electricity Board. With the installation of the ore preparation and sinter plant, which required 1MW of electricity to run, it was realised that the present power station was not capable of supplying the demand, thus a connection with the grid was essential. Since 1908, when the first turbine driven alternators were installed, Shelton had always supplied its own electricity at a generated voltage of 5,500 volts. Just before World War Two the National Grid substituted this voltage with 6,600 volts, thus Shelton had to have special equipment made when ordering new or replacement H.T. switch gear, transformers etc, which proved costly. Bearing in mind that the new Kaldo steel-making, Concast and Universal Beam Mill was in the pipeline, and would require some 3 to 4MW of electricity, it was decided to connect with the grid at 33,000 volts, using H.T. voltages at the new works, 11,000 volts and 3,300 volts. The ore preparation and sinter plant was connected at 11,000 volts.

A road weighbridge was installed in Etruria Road opposite the park. From its inception Shelton had relied on the railway for its raw material supplies and delivery of its finished products. However, by the mid 1950s road transport was being used mainly for the delivery of products from the 18" mill; also scrap metal was being delivered in ever increasing quantities by road. This was causing problems since, having no weighbridge, lorries had to use the public weighbridge in the centre of Hanley, situated at the rear of the meat market as it was then, in the area opposite the present MacDonalds. This wasted time and proved costly, so the Etruria weighbridge was installed, and was big enough to take long lorries which would be used in the future to transport steel from the 32" mill.

1960 saw heavy machinery clearing the site to make way for the building of a new steel making plant and universal beam rolling mill, that were to make Shelton the leading steel producer in Europe. In 1964 the revolutionary Kaldo steel making and Concast continuous casting plant started production, along with the universal beam mill, which had closed circuit television and computer control, and Shelton became the most up-to-date works in Europe. There were 4 concast machines, one of them being the largest of its type in the world, casting blooms of 18" x 14" up to 24" x 17", and also slabs of up to 42" x 8". The 32" mill closed in 1964.

NATIONALISATION OF THE STEEL INDUSTRY

The steel industry was nationalised in 1951, de-nationalised in 1953, and finally nationalised in 1967, there having been fairly rapid governmental changes in this period. Lord Mechett was in charge of the nationalisation and rationalisation of the steel industry, but when he died suddenly he was replaced by Dr Monty Finniston, who was to have close dealings with Shelton Bar. (The workers called him Dr Finishem!) Shelton was nationalised on a technicality, for though considered too small to meet the normal annual output for nationalised industries, it was squeezed in by adding to it the output of the Shotton Works.

Within a few months, in May 1968, the coking plant closed due to the installing at Shotton of their own blast furnace and coking ovens, with the loss of 400 jobs. But the men accepted this as a logical rationalisation. A further closure came in June 1971 when the 18" mill finished work, followed by the Construction Department in 1976. Sadly, in this decade of the 1970s the B.S.C. decided that Shelton was too small a producer of steel to be viable and

The last cast from No 6 blast furnace just after midnight 22/6/78

planned to close down the steel making section, and bring cold steel from Scunthorpe to be worked at the Shelton Mill. This would mean that a large part of the works, i.e. the blast furnaces and steel making section would become redundant. The familiar red glow in the sky when the furnace was being tapped or the slag taken away to be tipped would be no more.

An Action Committee was formed to try to keep the works going, and its members did sterling work travelling to London to meet members of B.S.C. and the Government, to put their case for carrying on work at Shelton. They were ably led by Mr. Ted Smith, time clerk on the works, and received support and praise for their efforts from many famous people. The Victoria Theatre-in-the-Round staged their highly successful show *Fight for Shelton Bar*, which they had in their repertoire for the 12 months of 1974. This fight went on from 1971 to 1978, and the workers continued to make the works one of the most profitable in the country, even when the B.S.C. began taking business away from Shelton and loading them with non-profit making orders! Even after profitable sections had been closed down in the 1970s, they had made a profit by reducing manning levels and meeting orders on time.

Finally a section of the workers were offered redundancy pay, and this led to the whole plant closing down, and putting workers against workers for the first time in the long history of the firm. It was a bitterly sad time for all.

Even under nationalisation Shelton Bar tried to maintain its "family firm" tradition: apart from an enforced stoppage of 3 days in 1972 there had not been a strike since 1886! (Not counting the General Strike of 1926.)

Sir David Davies said that they had the *"best management/worker relationship he had ever seen in 40 years in the industry"!* At one stage one of the leaders of the Action Committee, Mr. Bernard Wright, had gone toting for business round local firms, and had come up with a potential list of 600 firms within a thirty mile radius who would be willing to buy from Shelton - the sort of firms who used to ring up when Shelton was a private firm and receive their order the same day! One customer, only 200 yards from Shelton's main gates, had had so much trouble getting an order from B.S.C. that he had bought from Belgium. When he received the order it was stamped "SHELTON", and it had cost him £164 a ton, compared to £92 which it would have cost him straight from Shelton!!

Another example of the good service always given by Shelton Bar was for an order of steel to build a hotel in Las Vegas. The firm had the order on board ship in 24 hours, it being 1,000 tons. The American firm involved said that they had never had such excellent service, and could they cancel their B.S.C. contract and deal direct with Shelton instead! But of course they couldn't. The most amazing thing about the "Fight for Shelton Bar" during the 1970s was the 100% support given by the Labour Party and the Government, even to the extent of having Lord Beswick to look into the closure situation, and accepting his report that under no circumstances should the works be shut! When it came to the crunch, the Labour Party, which was in government, sat back, making the statement: *"We cannot interfere with the workings of the British Steel Corporation!"* So much for politicians! What a turn-around! Thus iron and steel making at Shelton was shut down on 23rd June, 1978. Many people thought that it was the complete end of the steel works, but that was not the case as will be seen in ensuing chapters.

LAST DAY WORKS 'SCENE'

The Blastfurnacemen's Union did a deal with B.S.C. in which a very large redundancy package was offered. It was a Wednesday evening and the blastfurnacemen were locked in the works canteen doing the deal with the B.S.C. The remainder of the workforce not on duty stood in Cobridge Road (where the canteen was), and the road was blocked to traffic. It had been agreed that there should be a silent protest, no placards or banners, and certainly no violence. All management were to be present to keep an eye on their staff.

There was a nasty moment when an ITV film crew arrived, handed out placards and attempted to incite the men to rowdiness. They took a few shots (photographic!), but were then moved on, leaving a few placards behind - "you always find a sister Anna who will carry a banner!"- the saying goes. T.V. so often gives the wrong impression: when the Midlands ITV News was relayed at 10.00p.m. it showed the placards, and the commentator stated: "There were riotous scenes outside Shelton Steel Works tonight as the blastfurnacemen discussed the future of the works with B.S.C." But here was no riot; people stood chatting and it was like a big family gathering, many wives being there and one policeman. He had been sent to keep the traffic flowing, but had given up and stood talking with the Shelton Security Men.

When the meeting broke up and it was learnt that the blastfurnacemen had accepted the package by a small majority, the atmosphere was one of intense despair - the end had come! The blastfurnacemen emerged from the canteen, some with bowed heads. A passageway was made for them as they crossed the road to get to the carpark opposite. There was the odd "boo"and someone shouted "Judas", but mostly the crowd was silent. All made their various ways home utterly dejected, like lost sheep.

The next morning on the works there was great bitterness. The blastfurnacemen were "sent to Coventry", and for the first time the family bond at Shelton was broken. The B.S.C. had set worker against worker.

Management met and it was decided to close down the iron and steel making as soon as possible. During the afternoon Mr Roland Marks gave the instruction to "damp down" the two on line blast furnaces. Nothing happened! There was a flame of rebellion! The blast furnace middle management, foreman and a handful of workers had decided to ignore the instruction and work on regardless! This constituted a very serious problem as it was a very dangerous situation to run blast furnaces with an inadequate work force. Should problems arise that would cause a furnace to explode there would be tremendous loss of life.

As management were involved, the Committee Members of the Steel Industries Management Association, Shelton Branch (of which Les Hall was one), were called in to see if they could resolve the situation. There was no possibility that such a small workforce could keep two blast furnaces running for more than 24 hours, as sleeplessness would be telling on them. It was tricky, as the Committee admired the men's stand; however they began talks with the blastfurnace middle managers, pointing out the dangers and hopelessness of a prolonged run, as B.S.C. would ultimately cut off raw supplies. At first their pleading fell on deaf ears, and the typical Shelton attitude of *"we shall not give in"* prevailed. After hours of talking the "rebels" finally gave in at 2.30 in the morning, and work proceeded in damping down the furnaces.

Next morning a management meeting reviewed the situation, closed down the Kaldo and Continuous Casting plants, and after discussion Les closed down the Power Station, deciding to rely solely on supplies from the M.E.B. The following morning Les visited every sub-station associated with the shut down plants, (blast furnaces, ore crusher, ore preparation sinter plant, Kaldo and Continuous Casting), to ensure that all main circuit breakers were in the locked open position. Then he went on to the Power Station and instructed the Supervisor to shut the station down. This was far from an easy thing to do, it was an action that put an end to 70 years generation at Shelton Bar. A great chapter came to an end, and the Power Station became just a switching station for the M.E.B. until its demolition.

Within a week all the blastfurnacemen were paid up and gone, and during the next 14 days the Kaldo and Continuous Casting plant men's Unions struck a deal with B.S.C. and they were gone too. The end had arrived for these men, but for the Management there were still months of struggle and uncertainty towards a massively reduced operation on the Sheton Bar site.

The beginnings of the new plant in the 1960s.

Union gathering in the 1960s. Mostly shop stewards at the works. The central figure in white coat is Sir David Davies, Gen. Sec. of Iron and Trades Confederation. The man far left was the manager of the steel casting plant.

Early 1900s. From left to right: Original No 6 blast furnace, beam blowing engine house, hydraulic engine house with hydraulic accumulator, open hearth steel furnaces with chimney stacks in front.
The original Wedgwood pottery is in the right background.

'Batt' boiler c.1950s. This provided steam from pulverised low grade coal.

From the left to right: Mill sheds, concast plant, sinter plant, ore stocking ground and ore crushing plant.

Weighbridge on the Grange - c.1920s. The Grange colliery is in the background.

Two of more of Alf Wakefield's fine pictures. The ingot charger, above,
and the cooling pits into which molten metal was poured as described by Les Hall.

Four
INCIDENTAL INFORMATION THROUGH THE YEARS

H.G. Wells visited Shelton Bar, when he stayed in Etruria in the 1890s whilst recovering from an illness. He was accompanied by his friend, William Burton, a ceramic chemist. Their favourite spot was Etruria Woods where they lay amongst the bluebells and surveyed the industrial scene. Perhaps it was here that Wells thought up his weird tale called *The Cone*, the story of a man's terrible demise in a furnace.

Inevitably there were plenty of tragedies at these works, especially in the early days, though it would not be in anyone's interest to elaborate too much. However one or two stories have a more general interest about them. About 1860 a man named Jones was trapped in machinery and died. He had been visiting the works and not working, and he was in his Etruria Volunteers uniform, so he was given a military funeral - he was the first of the volunteers to die. At the turn of the century some poor worker jumped into an open furnace and no trace of him was found. Blast was taken off the furnace and the local vicar read the burial service over it. It was recorded that a small boy of six, named Andrew Hollins, was overcome by fumes on one of the slag heaps - dangerous places - and was burnt to death; he was buried in Etruria churchyard on October 29th 1865.

During the Chartist Riots in the 1840s there was a serious threat to the furnaces and machinery at Shelton Bar. On August 15th 1842, a mass of local colliers demanding a fair day's wage met at Crown Bank, Hanley, and marched to the nearest coal and iron works. They did much damage to the partially completed works of Earl Granville, stopping engines and breaking windows. A lone Etruria policeman tried to intervene and was thrown into the pool, being held under water until he almost drowned! The rioters damaged houses and shops, and broke into buildings all over the district, including Hanley Police Station. More information about these riots can be found in the book *When I was a Child* by Charles Shaw, a potter of the last century, who really puts into perspective the terrible conditions that poor people had to endure in those days.

In the early years of the iron and steel industry, before and around 1900, molten slag was hauled away by horses, and there were often accidents to both men and horses, as the metal jolted from the ladles, causing terrible burns. A dispensary/infirmary was first established in Etruria in 1804, and the Hargreaves map of 1832 shows the infirmary in its new position. Later the men were taken to the North Staffordshire Infirmary at Hartshill in carts lined with straw. Sometimes with a badly burned worker the driver would call at the Railway Inn for brandy for him. The horses were well cared for too: one driver, John Wilson, would sit up all night nursing burnt horses.

From 1824 horse racing was held during "Wakes Week", the first week in August, over a mile course on a 50 acre site, made in the time of Josiah II, to the east of Etruria Hall. It stretched towards the Grange at Cobridge. It was an excellent position in summer, but bleak in the winter. A quote from an old history of Staffordshire says:

"The racecourse is on Mr Wedgwood's estate at Cobridge, where the grandstand was built about 9 years ago by subscription and a number of booths by various individuals. The course is one mile in circuit and the races are attended by an immense multitude of people

from all parts of the Potteries and by some of the neighbouring gentry......"

Potters and their families enjoyed a pleasant day out, the air being clean and fresh and no smoke yet. The last race meeting held was on August 4th 1841. From 1850 races were held at Boothen, Stoke. Eventually (within living memory) the circuit was used for rabbit coursing.

The Racecourse Pits (coal mine) were opened on the racecourse c. 1870, by Earl Granville to the east of the Hall. I am indebted to well known local writer, the late Fred Leigh, for the following:

"five shafts were sunk, to supply coal and iron ore for the works. Number 1 and 2 shafts were closed at an unknown time, and number 5 during the coal strike of 1921. Number 3 continued to produce coal and iron ore. Number 4 was used mainly as an upcast shaft for expelling air from number 3. This was a very wet pit, due mainly to the closing of the Grange Pit. Severe flooding took place, which resulted in the closing of the Racecourse Pit in 1941-2. There could have been a disaster, because 300 men and boys worked there on the day shift. Fortunately the flooding took place at night. Within a few hours the water reached three quarters of the way up the shaft! The pit was located somewhere near to where Morrisons' supermarket is situated today."

It was the intention of the Shelton Company to re-open this pit at a later date and in 1944 a submersible pump, 500KVA transformer (5.5KV/440V) and associated switch gear were purchased in preparation. However, this plan was abandoned in 1945, and the pump was sold to Severn Trent Water Authority. The electrical equipment was installed in the Blast Furnaces Hydraulic Engine House, to power a 50 HP motor and eliminate a steam engine.

In about 1898 a tip had been started behind Etruria Hall, which became known as the Racecourse Tip, and it became a great eyesore! This was not a colliery tip but contained all the iron and steel waste, old furnace bricks and rubble.

As the years wore on there was much subsidence in Etruria and the contours of the village changed drastically. Eventually the pottery works were many feet below the level of the canal and much shoring up of buildings had to be done. Etruria's Saint Matthews Church suffered serious structural damage, and Shelton workers helped to put some of the trouble right. There was a good rapport between the church and the Shelton workers and in 1926, the year of the general strike, 25 of the workers offered to clean and paint the church. One of them found a shilling and the vicar said that he could keep it, and also any more money that the men might find. I guess they were thrilled, because altogether they found 17/6, a goodly sum in those days, which would certainly have been welcome to the poor men and their families. I remember the church being demolished when I was a girl - strange things happened there and it was no longer safe. As a matter of interest, when the church was demolished the stained glass windows were removed and packed up by Shelton workers: where they went to is anyone's guess!

I was surprised recently to learn from a childhood friend that her father had worked at Shelton Bar, and often he came home with bandaged hands and face, when he had been burnt: I had not even realised that he worked there as did my dad, although we only lived a couple of doors apart! Also another friend, who lived in the next street, told me her dad had been a chimney builder there. Unbeknown to us kids he was a great joker: When he had helped to complete a particularly high chimney, he had seriously wanted to take her to the top of it in a hoist, and she was game. However her mum had put her foot down and vetoed the idea. Shame really for it would have been a great adventure.

It seems funny that we children knew so little about our fathers' work, yet I suppose we were too immersed in our childhood games - and perhaps our fathers were too busy working. Certainly we can feel grateful that we had such hardworking parents.

The coking plant and the Racecourse colliery tips, 1950s.

Shelton Iron and Steel Co 1950s, loaned by Mr J Ward who was a foreman in the coking plant. The Wedgwood potworks can be seen far right.

Five
DANGERS AT WORK

'Toilers in the mine and mill,
Toilers at the furnace-blaze,
Long forgotten, living still,
All Thy servants tell Thy praise.'

(from 'For the brave of every race' by George Wallace Briggs)

Many, many folk in our industrial city have memories of the accidents and hardships that their fathers and grandfathers suffered at work, and made light of - to spare their children's fears! The stoicism and courage of these generations of workers should amaze us in this present age of endless complaints and grabbing for 'compensation' at the merest hurt or stress, a word unheard of by these stalwarts of the past!

Nowhere is this more true than in Etruria, where family togetherness is still strong, even though the village itself has all but disappeared in the sprawling modernisation of the area, as Ernest Warrilow predicted many years ago. The Etruscan community was tight knit for two and a half centuries, the workforce a dedicated, tough and genial whole, imbued with the rough sense of humour needed to see them through. The many hazards in the heavy and dangerous occupations from the early days, right up to recent times, caused families to cling together for support.

Bill and Ethel Eaton recall how their father, also called Bill, had come home from Shelton Bar, about 1935, with his hands and his face heavily bandaged. They did not know why, being children, but learnt much later that he had been burned in a blowout at the coking plant. He healed beautifully and always had a good complexion his son said. Later he had the misfortune of losing all four fingers of his right hand, ripped off by a machine, and he was

Shelton bar workers c.1920s.

off work for a long time. There were no wages, only what ever 'club' insurance a man might have, and no compensation, but eventually he was allowed back to work again as keeper of the crossings gates at the bottom of Cobridge Road - he must have let my own dad through many a time! His son remembered what enormous muscles he had in his left arm, from turning the heavy wheel 'single-handed' to open and close the gates!

Charlotte, a widow for two years (2002), had come as a young lady from Liverpool to wed her sweetheart, Thomas Booth, in 1954. He worked on 'The Bar', and before she knew him he had suffered a horrendous accident there. Working high up on a crane, he had come down rapidly to help with someone who had suffered a heart attack at ground level, and another man was sent up to work the crane. This person accidentally caused a live electric cable to drop from the crane, and this 'snaked' around Thomas and threw him a considerable distance! Amazingly he did not die, but suffered a fractured skull and burns; he was unconscious in hospital for a week. Yet, after three weeks in hospital, he signed himself out! Seven or eight weeks later he was back at work. He completed 44 years with the firm before retiring due to ill health. They never had any children.

A friend, Joyce (nee Clowes), who lived in Garibaldi Street as a girl, told me that two of her uncles worked at Shelton Bar, Joe and Harry Titley. She was quite young when Uncle Harry was driving an overhead crane and a workman climbed onto the gantry and the crane crushed him to death. He was a Mr Leese, who came from Salem Street. Uncle Harry was devastated by this accident to a fellow worker and he never quite got over it.

Joyce's Grandad, George Machin, and a cousin, Ronald Jackson, also worked on the Bar. She said they often heard of very nasty accidents and there were hundreds of minor ones. One friend who went to work as an apprentice there in his teens lost an eye in an accident. The control room, as the ambulance room was called, was constantly busy, and my own father often spoke with great respect for the people who worked there, especially Sister Boulton, who became a legend. She is still alive, in her nineties now, and living in sheltered retirement. My Dad often had to go to the control to have bits removed from his eyes, a continuous hazard for all the workers there. Joyce remembered vividly how hectic life was in Etruria village during the 1940s to 1960s - at the changing of shifts bus loads of men and boys arrived from Hanley and Newcastle, and droves of men came along Forge Lane to catch buses back home.

John (Jack) Whitehouse, Etruria born and bred and now in his eighties, told me that his father, of the same name, worked at Shelton Bar from about 1914 to 1944, as an engineer ram driver on the coking plant. This machine opened the oven doors for the finished coke to be pushed out. In about 1930, Mr Whitehouse saw that a cable which was part of the opening mechanism was coming off its drum, and set about replacing it. It whipped off the four fingers of his right hand and ripped up his arm tearing all the muscles! Even so he managed to prevent the breakdown of the coking system. He spent several weeks in hospital and a long time recuperating at home, the only income being from the Welfare Fund penny-a-week scheme, run by the workers. He had been a keen bowls player, and of course, when he returned to health, with his right hand ruined he had to try to bowl with his left, but he could not wipe the bowl as is usual practice in bowls, and it was most frustrating for a man who had been a great bowler. The Shelton firm did not want to take him back, but agreed to re-instate him after about 18 months of 'negotiation'. He worked as a general labourer for a while and then returned to the same job which had caused the injuries - an act of monumental courage!

Two photos from the 1920s.

George Forster of Etruria was a blast furnace foreman for many years. His daughter Doris went to work in the office which dealt with the pig iron section, and she told me of a long shed where vats of molten iron moved along. One tipped and engulfed a man who was working nearby, an indescribable end! Her dad was called the keeper and he often had awful burns and scalds. Her mother used to scrub his moleskin trousers for him and she actually made his protective under-the-arm shirts for work. This fine lady had actually been born in the Armoury Cottages on the works.

Doris's grandfather also worked on the Bar, when unions were in their early days and not condoned. Grandad had been a big union man and he eventually got the sack for his activities. This is another of many examples of generations following each other onto the steelworks.

Doris told me that there were many offices all over the works for the various departments or 'shops' as they were called. She was often in touch with the Shotton works, in regard to the constitution of the pig iron and amounts produced weekly for example. She married another Shelton worker in 1942, and became Mrs Shepherd. She took 3 years off in the 1950s when she had her son, and then came back to a different department until the shut-down in 1978. She remembered when an outside contractor was called in to lower a chimney and was overcome by carbon monoxide fumes, blown across from the furnaces by a strong wind, and fell to his death below.

Len Jones, the story of whose rescue is recorded in the Alf Wakefield chapter later, was deaf. When he wasn't using his hearing aid he kept it in his waistcoat pocket. It seems amazing that a person with this disability should have been working at the top of a furnace! When he was dragged out from the covering round the top of the furnace, he was unconscious, overcome by the fumes, and badly burnt. The doctor, when he arrived at the control room, declared him dead from electrocution. This was incorrect and Alf Wakefield made this clear at the coroner's court, which he attended on behalf of the management.

The canal claimed many victims through the years, and two workmen lost their lives by drowning within a short space of time. One, an erector foreman and very good at his job, had enjoyed a heavy drinking session at the pub, then went over to get fish and chips from 'Florry' Ball's shop, stuffing them in his pocket to eat when he got home. He must have tottered into the water as he wended his way back along the canal. His body was retrieved next day, with his supper still tucked inside his pocket. The other worker, a steam crane driver, was cycling into work from Longport, in thick fog, along the side of the canal, and unfortunately went straight into the water.

In the late 1960s a man was drafted into the Demag mill on shift with Alf Wakefield, from his usual work in the 32" mill. It was the day shift and at 1pm, not properly aware of the danger, he failed to duck as the boom charger was moving a beam along. He received a blow to the head which killed him instantly. It was a dreadful scene and all the workers were extremely upset. The foreman, Jack Steele, asked Alf to deal with the clearing up and to assist the factory inspector with his enquiries. He explained exactly how the accident had occurred, and even stood where the man had been when the accident happened, for the official works photographer to record the scene for the coroner's court. One feels that Mr Wakefield must have had nerves and strength as strong as the steel he produced!

A young man named Ronald Thompson, aged 28, a respected member of Alf's team, was electrocuted while doing maintenance work in a high tension cubicle. He had worked at

Shelton from boyhood and had married a girl from the hall offices 4 years before. They had only moved into a new house in Clayton a month previously and had a 6 weeks old baby son.

Alf also mentioned an outside contractor, who died by electrocution on the works. He also told me about a couple of workers who had served in the trenches in World War 1. One, Nobby Dale, had been a 16 year old drummer boy and, as he went round the works, he was always whistling and walked as if he were still an army drummer boy. Another man had been in the trenches and suffered terribly afterwards, being unable to sleep during the night. He needed medication and a special dispensation from the works allowed him to work all nights.

Mr Stan Metcalfe began work at Shelton as a brickie's labourer. He was a keen photographer and when the management saw what excellent photos he took they asked him to become the official works photographer, and set him up in a little cabin of his own. He was the man responsible for all the photos in the 1964 new works commemorative brochure, of which a copy was presented to every Shelton Bar workman at the time. His photographs recording the scenes of fatal accidents were examined at coroner's courts by the jury, who were also allowed to ask witnesses questions.

When the new Kaldo and Demag works, costing £20 million, were up and running in the mid 1960s, they were the first of the kind in the whole world, and interest was intense. People came to visit the works from many different countries, and the maintenance electrician shift team leaders acted as guides to show them round and explain the set-up. Alf took round Japanese engineers, and many others, including a Canadian electrical and mechanical engineer, who spent three days with him. He was so impressed with everything he saw, that he offered Alf a job to help him set up a similar works in Canada. He was particularly interested in how cranes were used to keep the whole works in good repair, and he actually took a copy of Alf's work shedule. But Alf did not take up his offer.

One complete electrical maintenance shift including two men who died on the works. The mess room behind must have been near the canal, for the boatees (the bargee wives) would come in to get their water from there. Tom Hollingsworth, Len Jones*, Ron Thompson*, George 'Shortie' Lea (foreman), Alf Wakefield.
* died on the works

Picture of the Loop Line train coming from Shelton Bar. Alf Wakefield.

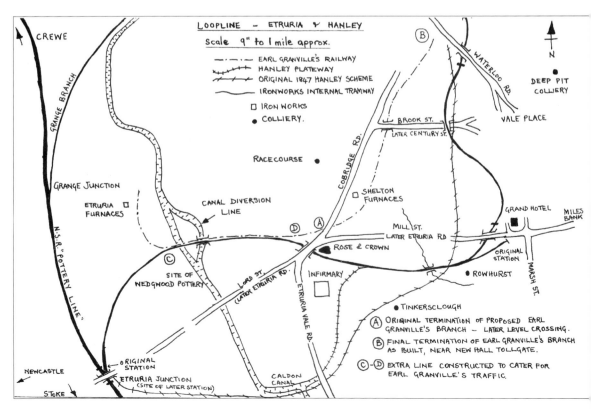

Six

THE RAILWAY AT SHELTON BAR

The following quotes from Alan C. Baker's extremely interesting book *The Potteries Loopline* are a good introduction to the railway system used by Shelton Bar.

"Etruria was hardly beautiful, but it was full of interest and activity, the gateway to a romantic world of mystery behind the steelworks. Part of the world looked on as unfavourable, but actually the very reverse to those who have taken the trouble to know it and love it!"

From foreword by J.R. Hollick:

"The loop was a difficult line to work in terms of gradients and curvature." *"....after an eventful and fascinating trip round the Potteries the line wound its way back to rejoin the main line just over seven miles from Etruria. ....it provided the best hour's entertainment that a local enthusiast and devoted potter born and bred could ever wish for!"* Alan Baker

THE RAILWAY AT SHELTON BAR

The railway system which served the works became quite indispensible. The first 'iron roads' in the area had been horse powered tram roads, linking limestone quarries, collieries and pottery works and the Trent and Mersey Canal. Earl Granville had an extensive system of narrow gauge tramways connecting various parts of the works internally, and the coal and iron mines serving them. Slag was hauled away from the iron furnaces by a fleet of horse drawn wagons - one shudders to think of the danger involved for man and beast. A 'plateway' was built in 1802 by the Canal Company to serve Hanley and later the iron works. This left the canal at its Cauldon branch junction and ended at the northern end of the town, being known as the Hanley Tramway.

The rail vehicles at Shelton Bar consisted of slag bogies, pig bogies and wagons. Later the lines were converted to standard gauge when the North Staffs Railway came into being and locomotives worked the lines. Shelton Bar was the first iron works to have a rail link. Earl Granville's first recorded locomotive dated from 1856, but he certainly had one prior to that since it is stated that in 1852 he took his loco onto the North Staffs Line to visit friends at Sandbach! He was reprimanded for this because he had not sort permission to use the line!

It is intersting here to give a brief record of the coming of the railway to North Staffordshire. The first line to pass through the county, the Grand Junction Railway (G.J.R.), between Birmingham and Warrington, and starting in 1837, missed the Potteries completely by five miles to the west! This was infuriating for the manufacturers of the area who desperately needed better transport, and they pressed hard for railway access. The inception of the North Staffs Railway was in 1846, and it took the Staffordshire Knot as its emblem, and became known affectionately as 'The Knotty'. When it opened in 1848 it missed the three pottery towns on hills, Tunstall, Burslem and Hanley, as well as the nearby market town of Newcastle! The locals were incensed! Meanwhile the Railway Company had bought out the Canal Company (an obligation put on them by a government act) and was reaping all the profits, having acquired almost all local means of transport!

Thereafter much agitation and many battles ensued at local and national level to obtain a rail link between all the towns. The idea of a loopline to include the beleaguered towns grew, and the "Potteries Loop Line" received the Royal Assent in 1865, though it was not completed with all its branches until 1875. It went from Kidsgrove to Etruria, passing through Tunstall, Burslem, and Hanley on its way. It was to serve the area wonderfully for 101 years, before being completely closed down after a "lingering death" in 1969.

The main railway line from Stoke to the north runs against the Fowlea Brook, whose course had been altered to accommodate it at Etruria. The first station here was built on the north side of the Newcastle to Hanley road just over the Wolstanton border and opened in 1848. It was later rebuilt along with stationmaster's house and cottages for railway workers. (A friend of mine, whose father was a railway inspector, grew up in one of these cottages). In 1862 the station was rebuilt on the south side of the road bridge, when the first part of the Loopline opened, and exists there to this day, though now it is unmanned and soulless.

Earl Granville's mineral line curved off to the right beyond the first Etruria Station, a single track on a heavily graded spur, sweeping east and then north-east, serving the Etruria furnaces then under construction, and other parts of the works, and connecting with the iron and coal mines that supplied them. Another section connected the Shelton furnaces and Hanley Deep Pit, and this was the longest line in use. It crossed Waterloo Road at the Granville Crossings, the gates controlled from a very high signal box. All were in use by 1866.

The works lines at Etruria ran parallel to the Loopline, but had been there first. The Earl was granted running rights into the Etruria Goods Yard, where traffic was exchanged, and another works line was built between the years 1865-75 straight into the Goods Yard.

The line from Etruria through the works had a difficult climb out of the valley and had to cross over the canal by the Wedgwood Pottery Works by means of a drawbridge, which proved problematic from the start. Traffic was heavy and as early as 1854 engineers had to re-lay some sections of this bridge. Later, when the line was to be opened to passengers, the canal itself had to be diverted by 104 yards east! Many of the Earl's lines crossed the Loop Line at various points, and the whole must have been an immensely complicated (and interesting) system. Works traffic never used the main lines, and all works lines were officially referred to as the 'third lines'.

Earl Granville was only the second manufacturer in the country to use locomotives and he soon had a fleet of them working his lines. To quote Alan C.Baker again:

"As the train turned sharp right on leaving the main line at Etruria, it commenced its torturous climb of over one mile, with gradients as steep as 1: 41 with several reverse curves, towards Hanley. Little wonder that loads were limited, and the engines worked very hard. On this section to Hanley the observant traveller would be treated to views of the large Shelton Iron and Steel Works at close quarters and there would usually be several of the 'fussy' little four wheeled saddle tanks shunting around, and perhaps one of their larger six wheeled brethren. One might see ALICE, BUSCOT, GLENALMOND or the larger HARWARDEN amongst the four wheelers; DEENA and PEPLOW were the favourites among the six."

Eventually as many as 30 locos could be working at any one time, because there were 40 miles of track! The locomotives were much loved by workers and public alike, all having special names written on highly polished brass plaques on their sides. People who lived beside the track knew all the names (often those of directors' children, grandchildren, homes or estates for example), and could recognise their engines by their 'beat' and whistle. Drivers and firemen lovingly tended their engines and kept them beautifully clean and polished. My father painted some of them. Some of the well remembered ones were:

'Dubsey' - a combined shunting and steam crane engine, built by Dubs and Co.;

'Glenny' - short for Glenalmond, the name of the estate near Perth of the one time Shelton M.D. Alexander Henderson (later Lord Faringdon). This loco was built in 1912 and lasted for 60 years. It was different from the passenger locos, being sturdy and tough and suited to the steep gradients and narrow curves on the Shelton Bar site.

'Hawarden' - built at Bagnall's of Stafford in 1940 (works no.2623), now in retirement on the Foxfield Preserved Railway. The name came from the late owners' (Summers) parent works near Chester.

'Peplow' - (works no. 1707), a coupled side tank, built by Hudswell Clarke in 1939, and named after the village where Shelton Director Mr Neville Rollason lived during the war.

'Cornist' - came from the same 'stable'and worked the line from Hanley Deep Pit.

'Alice' - (works no. 884), named after one of the womenfolk of the Leveson-Gower (Granville) family, one of the 'fussy' little four wheel saddle tank brigade, and built in Kilmarnock by Andrew Barclay in 1900. It lasted until October 1953!

Most of the locos were rebuilt at Shelton Bar at least once, or extensively overhauled. They were kept and maintained in the 'Old Office Yard', Hanley, adjacent to the Loop Line (reached by a bridge over the Loop Line north of Hanley Station).

'Dubsey'did service for 70 years on Shelton Bar, a crane tank engine, with a fixed jib, which spun round 360 degrees and was a railway crane used to lift loads of up to 5 tons. It started work in 1901 and went on until 1973! It was a 'maid of all works' and was rebuilt several times, being converted to oil firing in 1961. It was bought by East Somerset Railway and changed back to coal firing, being last in steam in 1985. Now at the end of the century it has returned permanently to the area, and will be on show at the Foxfield Light Railway, Blythe Bridge, courtesy of Mr David Scragg.- obviously a man who recognises 'class', for this is the only Dubs crane in Britain and a unique piece of railway history! Hopefully it will be in working order and in steam again to celebrate its centenary in 2001. There will certainly be some old faithfuls from Shelton Bar along to see it!

Newcastle Station was on the road from Etruria to Newcastle and is now gone.

Shelton Bar.

Seven
THE MAKING OF STEEL GIRDERS by L. Rogan Hall
(Ed: An extract from a school magazine of the early 1930s I suspect)

The making of steel girders first starts at the Scrap Bank. Here pieces of scrap steel, such as parts of old cars, bicycles and so on are placed into long troughs. Four troughs are mounted on a low platform which is placed on a truck. This truck is then taken by rail to the Smelting Shop. The low platform with troughs on it is transferred to another platform by the side of a furnace. A machine called a charger picks up the troughs one at a time and deposits the scrap steel into the furnace. When a certain quantity of scrap metal has been deposited in one furnace, the metal is left until molten and has reached melting point.

Whilst the steel is being smelted, ingot moulds are being placed in the casting pit by a steam engine. When everything is ready, the furnace is 'tapped' and white hot metal runs into a ten-ton ladle. As soon as this is full, two small holes are opened in the bottom to allow the metal to run into moulds, where it is left to cool. The moulds are then taken away, leaving the ingots in the casting pit. A twenty-five ton electric crane now carries the ingots to some more furnaces. Here the ingot charger places the ingots in the furnaces until they are red hot - although white-hot would describe them better!

One at a time they are then taken on a truck to the mill to be rolled into shape. When it has been rolled into a long bar it is cut into several smaller bars to be heated up again!

When they have reached a certain temperature, the bars are sent, one at a time, to still more rollers, where they are made into girders etc. Long girders are cut into smaller ones while still red-hot and when cold are put into the 32" shed. Railway trucks come for them when necessary and they are sent to all parts of the world.

Mr Les Hall receiving an award
from Mr Field in 1967.

Starting work at Chatterley Whitfield colliery in the 1930s.

Some of the workers including Les (the one with the grin second up on the right).

Eight
STARTING WORK IN THE 1930s

In 1936 Leslie Hall, an enterprising lad of fourteen, heard his parents say that they didn't know how they were going to find a job for him, so without a word he went off and found one for himself! It was as a messenger boy, 'the lowest form of animal life', on Shelton Bar. The Headmaster at school let him leave before the end of the school year, to start his job.

Leslie had to be at work by 8.30am, and he was messenger boy for the Etruria Time Office, at the end of Forge Lane, where the Head Time Clerk, Mr Tom Mitchell, was in complete charge, having the power to 'hire and fire'. Leslie's work included cleaning and washing up after the night shift, making tea and putting up the tally board. Tallies were round metal discs with a number on, one for each employee; each man had to take his tally, and, at the end of his shift, post it through a letter box into the office, where it slid down a shute and onto a table, and the boy had to hang it back on the board. Sometimes these tallies shot dangerously across the room when men pushed them in, on purpose, very hard. They were used for clocking on and off. If a man did not turn up for a shift, the previous man had to stay and work on for the extra shift.

Of course Leslie had to take messages too, to different parts of the works. When he had to go into the iron and steel works he loved to stop and watch all the processes of the works going on. The older men used to rag him a great deal, good-naturedly, as most workmen do to youngsters. He used to watch the steel bars come along the skid bank, where the men used a mixture of tar and oil from buckets to make the metal skid along. They would chase him and cover his knees with the tar and oil, so every day he had to spend three quarters of an hour scrubbing the stuff off again. He was in short trousers, because his parents could not afford long ones for him! After a while his parents received a letter from the management, and his father said, 'What have you been up to at work, lad?' Leslie was apprehensive, wondering what he had done wrong, but the letter was just asking if they could buy him some long trousers, so that he would not be put through this torment every day.

In the rolling mill he watched the men expertly jumping over the hot iron bars, and was delighted when he was shown how to do it safely himself. Once, when he had been sent with a message, and had delayed to watch the steelmen on his way back, the boss questioned him about whether he had come straight back. When he answered in the affirmative the boss said he was telling fibs, because he had telltale evidence on him - whitewash across the back of his shoes! In those days there were no electric lights around the mills, and in order for the workers to see, the bottoms of the columns were constantly being whitewashed. If someone happened to be standing in the way their feet got whitewashed too! Leslie had to admit that he had been watching the men at work and the whitewash brush had caught him from behind!

On Friday afternoons Leslie had to fetch the wage books from the main offices in Etruria Hall. Messenger boys had to go in by the back way, which at that stage was at the west front of the imposing building. The first time he went in through the main hall and to the commissionaire's window Leslie felt very overawed. He asked for the books and was shown into a room where five immense leatherbound ledgers were waiting to be collected. He found he could barely lift one, let alone five! Somehow he managed to tuck one of these weighty volumes under each arm, and staggered forth on his return journey to the time office, a journey which usually took about ten minutes. By the time he reached the canal bridge he was exhausted, and realised this particular errand was going to take him ages. So he carefully hid the first two ledgers under the bridge, and dashed back to the Hall for two more, which he stacked alongside the others, while he returned for the fifth. Then the relay race began again to get the five precious books to the Time Office.

The Pay Office was adjacent to the Time Office, being the down stroke of the T shaped building with no outside exit, presumably for security reasons. Prior to the paying out of the wages it was scrubbed white by a labourer, and the messenger boy of course. This was done every week and the room was used solely for this purpose. Leslie's wage was 7/6, and at Christmas he was allowed to go round the works 'with a book', and each man gave him 1/2d.

A letter to the *Sentinel* concerning wages at the Shelton Bar blast furnace in the 1930s from G. Brown of Wolstanton says:

"I started work at the beginning of the 1930s. The wages were 6s. 7^1/2p for an 8 hour shift, we worked 3 shifts, with a 16 hour shift - 6am to 10pm - every third Sunday. There were no days off. The average weekly wage was approximately £2. 11s., so for a full year, working 8 hours every day for 365 days, one received the sum of approximately £132. This was for working outside, in all weathers, and the work was hard."

Leslie was alert and reliable, and was promoted earlier than after the usual year as messenger boy. In March, 1937, he was made a Hall office boy in the Purchasing Department, and so moved into that most interesting building, Etruria Hall, which was the hub of the busy iron and steel works. Here he had a most enjoyable time, for he loved the old building with its high ceilings and beautiful open fireplaces, and its interesting cellar, where he and the other office boys often helped the old caretaker with his buckets of coal for the open fires. In their spare moments they larked about down there, making their exit usually by the coal shute - until one day they were caught at it by the stern Works' Secretary, Mr. Batt!

The office boys had to be at work at 8.00 am to sort out the mail before the office staff arrived at 9.00, the senior office boy having the important job of receipt stamping all the incoming letters. But first of all each day, they had to line up and show their hands to Mr. Batt, who went along the line turning each boy's hands over to see if they were clean and ready for work! In the offices were high desks for the junior staff - Leslie had to climb up onto his stool - and lower ones for the seniors, and the boss also had his desk in the same office. The office boy had to address all the envelopes and clean and disinfect the telephones. After a while new tansad seats on wheels were introduced into the offices, and the boys had a great time whizzing round on these, when the bosses were not about, until a few got broken. Another favourite 'spare' time activity took place up in the loft, where the works records were kept: this was to wage war on each other with the fire extinguishers at full spurt! It makes you wonder how the records fared.

Once, Leslie recalled with undiminished glee, the junior clerks succeeded in persuading the young office typist by the name of Betty Birchall, to stand on her hands for them on one of the desks, and they were hugely enjoying the delightful sight of her down hanging attire, when the boss walked into the room! He was a stern disciplinarian, who viewed the scene with displeasure, and then said in a deep, firm voice, *"Len! Will! Put the good lady down and don't do it again!"*

Every day the office boys had to wait in the office until 5.00pm for the bosses to have signed the outgoing letters. Then they had to seal them and take them to the commissionaire, who put all the mail from the various offices into one large mail bag. This usually took till about 5.30pm, and then the boys would go straight off to night school. Leslie went three times a week for shorthand, typing and book-keeping. He and his friend ofen turned up for work on Saturday mornings in their scout uniforms, and after work would go straight off to their scouting activities.

The management at Shelton Bar were always noted for their consideration for the workers, and Leslie recalled with pleasure the happy times he had there in his early years with the firm. In return the workers displayed a great loyalty, and the atmosphere was almost that of a family business, although it reached a size when four and a half thousand men were employed there!

When war came in 1939 Leslie was ready to do his bit, and when he was old enough in 1940 he joined the Fleet Air Arm, and trained as an electrician, doing some of his service in Canada. In January, 1946, he was so eager to get back that he didn't have time to receive a demob suit, and returned to his job at Shelton Bar in uniform! His stay in Etruria Hall was short-lived, however, for after two weeks he was transferred to the Engineering Offices, where he became an electrical draughtsman, and later Design Development Engineer. When he married, his wife, Con, she was well aware even then that she was wedding not just Leslie, but Shelton Bar as well!

The messenger boy system was, until 1948, vital to the communication working of the Iron and Steel Works, because until that time the telephone system was very inadequate, with a total of only 12 telephones on the works, i.e. 3 at the Shelton end of the works, (18" mill, Boiler Shop, and Shelton Time Office), and 9 at Etruria (32" mill, Melting Shop, Blast Furnaces, Coking Plant, Basic Slag Works, Ambulance Room*, Boiler Plant*, Electric Shop*/Power Station, Etruria Time Office*). *Direct dialing between 6 p.m. and 8a.m.

A 50 line GPO telephone plug switchboard was situated on the second floor of Etruria Hall, manned by a lady from 8am to 6pm (two ladies shared this duty), and with the exception of the 12 phones mentioned above, all connections were within the Hall. In 1948 a 180 line automatic switchboard was purchased and sited in the Electric Shop adjacent to the Power Station, (this was moved to the Hall substation in 1957, when the Electric shop was re-sited at the North End of the Coking Plant, to make way for the power Station extension to accommodate No. 8 Set). Internal telephones were now available throughout the works complex and Etruria Hall. This was a revelation and from then on messenger boys were no longer employed. The inadequate GPO system was not altered until 1958, when an automatic switchboard was installed in Etruria Hall, replacing the manual unit, and thus GPO telephones appeared throughout the works. It seems incredible that Shelton being so much to the fore in many aspects should have turned its back for so long on such a wonderful means of communication. Les had noted, however, that they were not alone in this: when he joined the navy in 1940 he was surprised that a messenger boy system was still used in Barracks and on large vessels, such as the Prince of Wales, the Rodney, and Hood etc. My husband, an ex-sailor, commenting on this said that there were certain occasions when a personal messenger was to be preferred especially on board ship.

Etruria Hall, the main offices and main Shelton Bar entrance. Wedgwood Works is seen behind.

Below:
The Hall Field Pool where the sports ground was eventually made.
By Alf Wakefield.

Nine
SOME OF THE LAYOUT OF SHELTON BAR WORKS

The works were very self-contained, much ingenuity being used to supply necessary materials, tools, buildings and plant to pursue the industry with as little waste as possible.

The basic slag works, situated to the south west of Etruria Hall, were owned first by a private company - in fact, before the first World War, by a German firm, but afterwards were taken over by Shelton Bar. Basic slag was the scum remaining after the steel making, which was processed through a ball mill, where it was crushed to a fine powder. This was used as a fertiliser for the land. The Hall always had beautiful lawns surrounding it, and this was because they were fertilised continually by the fine dust coming from the slag works. I.C.I. had the selling rights for this product. Any spare ground on the works was always laid down as lawn and mown regularly, in order to prevent any accumulation of clutter, such as tin cans, oil drums, wire, rope etc. - such was the meticulous nature of later bosses, and an excellent thing too! Until the plant was fully mechanised in the 1950s big, buxom women were always employed to do all the trundling of the basic slag, in 1cwt. bags. These were about half the size of 1cwt. bags of cement, since it was twice as heavy, though not unlike cement in powdered form, except for its colour. The women used small hand jack trucks with ball bearing wheels (manufactured in Shelton's boilershop), to move the bags into the stock room or waiting railway wagons. The young lads on the firm, including Leslie, were told not to be cheeky to these hefty ladies, nicknamed 'Big Berthas'. This was always considered to be women's work - this comes as a bit of a surprise to folk unconnected with the works - until mechanised conveyor belts came into being.

Iron slag (the scum from iron making in the blast furnaces), on the other hand, was considered useless and always tipped. However, in 1946, the Tarmac Company installed a crushing and processing plant, making aggregates of various sizes from the iron slag, some of which were tarred for road making. This plant was situated on the north west side of Forge Lane, and operated, using up the vast quantities of tipped slag still available on the remaining Shelton Bar rolling mill site to the west of the canal, until Tarmac closed down the plant and dismantled it in 1995. It was not long before the Shelton Company also began to use these aggregates to make lamp standards, fencing posts, sleepers for railway lines and blocks for using in buildings on the works. There are houses in Brookside Close, Newcastle-under-Lyme, which have slag-block garden walls to this very day!

To the north east of the Hall was situated the old no. 2 Racecourse Colliery, somewhere hidden under the 1986 vast landscaping accomplished for the Garden Festival. This was closed in 1942, and one of the buildings was used as a piggery! After the war this same building was taken over for the construction of these iron slag based items. A mixture of slag and cement was used to create suitable material for them.

In about 1960 the large slag heap located behind the Hall, near to where the Racecourse Colliery had been, began to be levelled off, as part of Stoke's land reclamation scheme. Shelton began tipping further north towards The Grange, to level off the ground, using dirt and rubble from the furnaces, of which there were five; the brick lining had to be removed about every five weeks, so it is easy to imagine how much discarded brick and rubble needed to be dumped. In contrast the blast furnace linings had a seven or eight year life span.

A private company, the Slag Reduction Co., started up in the mid-60s, (for whom Les designed their electric sub-station), working in this northern area. They took steel slag and extracted any remaining metal by a process of crushing prior to delivery of the slag to the basic slag works. The extracted metal was sold back to Shelton Bar, to be used again in the furnaces. So nothing was wasted.

There was a very large coal stacking area to the north of the Racecourse Colliery for use during difficult times - strikes for example - over which a large gantry type crane transporter was used to distribute the coal. Other stores were also located there. All electrical supply cables in this area were overhead, and on a mound to the north end of the piggery building was a square steel cable tower rising 30 feet high, which had been designed by Les.

The coking plant laboratories and offices were situated behind the Hall at the northern end. Later these buildings became the computer centre of the works. A new I.C.I. computer built at Kidsgrove (Stoke-on-Trent) was installed, powered by generator equipment bought second-hand from Preston Corporation!

The coking plant closed down in the late 1960s. The plant covered a large area, having three coke oven batteries, two of which were constantly in use, and provided sufficient coke for the needs of the whole works. The third battery was kept always at the ready for use in emergencies. It is interesting to note that when John Summers installed their first blast furnace at Shotton, the coke they needed was supplied for many years by Shelton, until they had their own coking plant on site.

In the 1950s a coal blending plant had been installed, which mixed local slacks (ie.small pieces of coal with a low ash content), with Welsh slack, to give the required coal consistency for making the very hard and large coke needed in the iron making. The coke produced was some of the finest in the whole country. When the coal blending plant, which was fully automated, went into production, the coal washery plant was closed down as all coal slacks received were now washed at the colliery pit heads. The ancilliary plant which dealt with the many by-products of coal, such as naptha, benzine, tar, creasote, sulphuric acid etc., was situated between the batteries and the Hall. All the liquids were despatched by tanker or canal to the New Acid Co. and Staffordshire Chemical Co. (Shelton owned), for refining and sale.

There were two sulphate houses, both being used for the extraction of sulphuric acid and the production of sulphate of ammonia, which is good for the land. Les recalled how glad they were when plastic was first introduced for things like light fittings in the two sulphur houses, for previously the metal fittings only lasted a few weeks, due to rapid corrosion, the metal just melting away. I'm tempted to wonder what the atmosphere did to the people who had to work there!!

In front of Etruria Hall, which faces due west, were lawns, and into one of these near to the basic slag works was built an electric sub-station. This was during the 1950s when electrification was taking place for the surrounding area. It was built deep into the ground, so that from the Hall one could only see the flat roof, which was level with the lawn. Beyond the lawns there were the railway lines passing in front of the Hall and leading to the coking plant and marshalling yards.

Across these railway lines was a bridge from the bottom of the lawns over to the middle of the rail bank. This consisted of two banks, or rows, of metal posts 3 feet high, supporting long fixed rail racks. Onto these 60 feet long bullhead and flat bottom rails, produced in Shelton's 32" mill for general railway use, were 'skidded' for inspection. These had been slow cooled after hot rolling, to prevent stress fracture during annealing (toughening or strengthening) and then cold straightened by being fed through a 'mangle' exerting horizontal and vertical pressure to prevent distortion. The inspection was a lengthy business, carried out by one Shelton Inspector and one Railway Inspector, who walked along the top of each bar, visually examining every bit of it. Then the bar was turned over by a man at each end using a special hook, made at Shelton of course, and the inspectors examined the whole length on the other side. This was done scrupulously with every bar or rail, and took a great deal of time, all out in the open air, whatever the weather conditions might be!

After the inspection four men pushed each bar down the rails and into a wagon, made up to the required length to take 60 feet bars. This work was completely unmechanized and was very arduous. The last rolling of railway lines at Shelton took place in 1964, when the 32" mill was closed. It was not considered an economic proposition to roll these in the new universal mill at the North Works.

To the west of the rail bank were three sets of railway lines, then a wooden fence, on either side of which ran the Etruria to Hanley and Cobridge Loop Line - the 'Old Knotty' railway. This was 300 yards from Etruria Hall, and lower down ran within 20 feet of the steel smelting shop. Passengers on the Knotty would experience intense radiation heat within the coach, when the 'A' furnace was being tapped! Had the loop line not been there the steelworks, without a doubt, would have extended right up to Etruria Road, on the land that was used as a sports ground.

The use of water on the steelworks was very important. Much of this was taken from the canal, near to which the Power House was situated. It was taken in at three points, for the Power House, the Coking Plant Pump House and the Boiler Plant. If the water level was low in the canal this latter did not receive any water, which had to pass over a sill. At all the water intake sumps there were two rotary mesh screens fixed half in and half out of the water, which picked up all flotsom and prevented it entering the works. The water used had to be replaced in the canal, as most was lost in evaporation in boilers, cooling metal and washing coal etc. Therefore Shelton had pumps at two of the city sewage works, which directed water back into the canal. There were two at the Hanley Sewage Works on Leek Road, which were maintained and the running costs paid for by Shelton Bar. This works finished in the 1970s and part of the site is now occupied by the Stoke-on-Trent VI Form College (one of the first purpose built VI form colleges in the country). Later the new Staffordshire University took up more of this land. Two more pumps were used by Shelton Bar at Burslem Sewage Works, at the end of Middleport Lane. (I have a mental picture of two great tentacles stretching out into the city from the monster steelworks, to draw back nourishment to itself!)

When in the 1970s Burslem Sewage Works were completely renovated and new pumps installed, Shelton was able to make a valuable deal with Severn Trent Water Board: namely that Shelton electrical equipment should be situated within the Severn Trent Sub-station, with a wall separating this from the rest of the station, Shelton contributing to part of the sub-station building costs and the electricity for running the pumps connected to the Severn Trent supply. This eliminated a separate supply cable from the Midlands Electricity Board to the Shelton pumps, thus reducing capital costs and resulting in cheaper electricity charges to both Shelton and Severn Trent, as only one feeder cable and set of metering was required.

Increased supplies of water were needed in the 1950s, and this was drawn from Fowlea Brook, running through the valley at the Basford end. This water served many purposes within the blast furnace operation, and returned to the brook on a return cycle system, after passing through the Sedimentation Plant, where all the pollution, chemicals, etc were removed. It is interesting to note that in order to get the water to where it was needed, a tunnel had to be mined through the vast slag heap which lay to the north west of the Hall beyond the canal. When you consider the magnitude of this slag heap - 60 feet high, 20 feet wide at the top and 100 feet at the base - you realise the ingenuity and hard work required to create this passage for the water bearing pipes.

In the 1950s a new steel works laboratory was built on the main driveway to Etruria Hall. This then presented the problem as to how to get the steel taken from the furnace prior to tapping to the lab for testing, WITH SPEED, before it cooled. A messenger on foot was too slow. This was achieved admirably by a method similar to that used in olden day shops, to convey money to and from the cashier, ie by compressed air! Thus the samples were carried in rounded pots via the tubes to the laboratory in seconds. All this was designed by Shelton expertise, the route followed by the tubes being from the melting shop, through the casting bay, through the 32" mill, over the canal, past the south end of the Power Station, across the coking plant marshalling yard, past the north end of Etruria Hall, around the garages, down the side of the surgery and into the lab, a distance of $1^1/_2$ miles!

The garages, the test house, the engineering design offices and a completely equipped surgery with its own ambulance were all located on the east side of the Hall at the far end of the lawns

Many people thought that the whole of Shelton Bar closed down in 1978, years before the garden festival took place. However 480 people were still employed there, with a day and night shift operating. The Works Manager was Mr. William Davidson, and work continued in the rolling mill (Demag mill) producing steel girders and sections of renowned quality.

The works did their bit for the Festival by allocating a room for the festival workers, rent free, their only bill being for heating and telephone. Also they improved the area around the works, painting and landscaping, so that a decent background was provided on the works side of the festival ground. British Steel provided a work shop and materials for part of the festival sculpture programme, and access to the Garden Festival site over their land. Mr. Davidson said that they were only too pleased to help and thrilled with the transformation eight years on after the sad closure of so much of the works.

Ten
DESCRIPTIVE DETAILS FROM MR KEN SPODE

Ken Spode was Turbo-Blower House Superintendent for 30 years, until iron making ceased in 1978. He was in charge of turbines, air compressors, pumps and water circulation plants, with a team of maintenance workers under him. His interest in Shelton Bar and his love of photography combined to make him a mine of information about the iron making section of the works. Hopefully many people who lived with the experience of the noise and dirt of the works and yet felt pride in it, while knowing little about its processes, will be interested in the details he gives.

In earlier times, before safety gear was issued to the blast furnace men, the iron workers would wear ladies' felt hats, with the brims pulled down to protect their faces. Sometimes if there were feathers they would leave them on, so you can imagine there would be some fun along with the hard work! Later, safety gear consisted of green felt coats, aluminium polycarbonate head gear and wooden clogs, rather like elongated horse shoes. These were worn by men working on the blast furnace casting floor (in the early days-the pig beds).

They were given beer in buckets from the 'Lamb' pub at the end of Forge Lane, situated on the main road in the centre of Etruria village. This was to replace the moisture they lost in perspiration. Later it was changed to oatmeal water which did not go down half as well! Later still they had tea, and in hot weather salt tablets, which were big and fizzy and lemonade flavoured.

The headman in charge of the furnace was called 'the keeper'. The base of the furnace had about 20 feet of carbon brickwork lining, referred to in early days as 'the bare' or 'bear', to which the molten iron gradually worked its way down. Could this have been where the word 'keeper' originated?

There were 3 blast furnaces when iron making ceased (1978), not named, as present large furnaces are, but numbered 1, 4 and 6, this being due to the past existence of smaller intermediate ones. They were huge structures, up to 100 feet high, with steel rings at the lower part, and steel casing higher up, totally lined with close fitting fire brick. This lining was cooled higher up by 'cigar coolers', long water cooled cast iron pipes which were cemented into the lining; and lower down by copper 'cooling blocks', again water cooled.

At the top of the furnaces were the 'double bells' through which the charge or 'burden' was dropped into the furnace. The top part was opened to receive the charge and then closed before the inner part opened, so as to prevent the release of pressure from inside the furnace. Sometimes the charge did not slip down easily and a 'void' would be created. When the burden did suddenly slip there would be a great increase in pressure and the lids at the top of the safety outlet tubes at the top of the furnace, called (curiously) 'candles', were forced open to emit clouds of bits of coke, redhot ironstone, dust and furnace gases. The impressive effect of this 'charge slip' on the surrounding district has been described in another chapter.

Number 1 furnace, being the largest, had four candles and numbers 4 and 6 had two. The charging system at Shelton was unique. Most systems are of the inclined hoist type, while Shelton consisted of vertical hoists situated on either side of a long 'bunker' from which coke, iron ore and limestone was fed into 'scale cars' to be weighed. These containers were then positioned under vertical hoists, the charge lifted to the height of the furnace by means of a continuous wire rope system, transported horizontally to the furnace top and lowered into the 'bell'.

At ground level the furnaces were 'blown' with 'hot blast' (900 deg.c.), through cast iron 'blow pipes' fitted into water cooled copper 'tuyeres', these being spaced round the circumference of the furnace at eye-level (at a volume of 30,000 cuft. per minute!). Looking along the 'blow pipe' by means of the blue glass 'eyepiece' one could see the iron smelting. The oxygen in the hot air reacted with the coke, iron ore and limestone to form the molten iron, and slag formed on top. Periodically this slag would be tapped off into a large 'slag ladle' through the 'slag notch'. This hole was higher and smaller than the iron tapping hole and situated approximately diametrically opposite. The 'slag notch' consisted of a large water cooled cast iron 'jumbo cooler' into which fitted a water cooled 'intermediate' cooler, followed by an even smaller water cooled 'pee-pee' cooler. The centre in this was sealed from the molten slag by means of a 'stopper', a long steel bar with a coned copper stopper at one end, rather like a cork in a bottle - but somewhat hotter!

The ladles of molten slag were pulled in later times out of the 'bogey hole' by locomotive -earlier steam, later diesel - and taken to be tipped at the slag heap. This of course is what caused the well-remembered glow in the sky.

The pig iron was tapped approximately every 3 or 4 hours, from the iron tapping hole, into firebrick lined ladles. Tapping in the early days was carried out by men driving an iron bar with a sledge hammer into the clay sealing the hole until the iron began to flow out. Later hand held pneumatic drills, and finally fixed drills were used, these drilled until the red glow of iron could be seen, and when everything was ready, a small piece of coal was thrown into the drill hole and an oxygen lance used to burn through to the molten iron. The lance was quickly withdrawn and the iron flowed into the 'runner', a dry sand lined channel which

Tapping of the furnace. Molten metal is running into the sand beds.

diverted the iron into the ladles. These ladles were then transported by rail to the 'steel works', where the iron was converted into steel.

Earlier 'pig iron' was run from the furnace into 'pig beds'. These were series of narrow channels (described elsewhere) leading from the main runner, called 'the sow' - hence the name 'pig iron'! Later iron was made into 'pigs' at the 'pig casting machine', to be sold to other firms or stocked.

Hot air for the furnaces was produced nearby in large cylinders filled with a honeycomb of firebrick, heated up by burning blast furnace gas inside, and blown into the furnaces via the tuyeres. Afterwards the gas, now mostly carbon monoxide but with other gases too, was led off by tubes to the gas cleaning plant. It passed through 'scrubbers' to remove dust and grit, which then dropped through a hopper into a waggon for removal. The men who did this job could literally not be seen because of all the filth in the air, and one wonders how they survived even a day.

Needless to say, the noise as well as the dirt in all these processes was intense and constant. Another terrible job was when a furnace needed to be relined, usually about every 4 years, when a group of men called 'the wrecking gang' had to climb inside and break down all the very hard and heavy brickwork and remove it all - no masks, no protective clothing and low pay. Yet these men worked with a will and a joke, as the photos show: there was team spirit as they toiled! The replacing of the above mentioned tuyeres was another very hazardous job: their copper ends sometimes burnt off, and the tube had to be removed and a new one inserted. Blast had to be taken off while the men did this extremely hot, dangerous and heavy work; each tube weighing about a quarter of a ton!

The turbines worked by high pressure steam, which then went to the cooling towers and pools, these being situated on the slag heap, quite large and deep. There were overhead jets from which the water sprayed out and then fell back into the pools. In the winter this spray water got blown about and when it was very cold froze on nearby pipes, some of which fractured causing enormous problems. The winter of 1963 was a particularly bad one, and some of the pictures of the resulting freeze up are quite astounding. It was a highly complicated matter to get everything going again.

The actual lighting of a furnace consisted of stacking straw and old wood inside, including old railway sleepers, with a charge of coke on top, all soaked in paraffin, then a long rod with paraffin soaked material wrapped round the end and ignited was thrust into the tap hole to start the fire. The furnace would take days to be brought up to heat before the iron making could be resumed.

As I found with other people who worked at Shelton Bar, Ken Spode was a dedicated man, fascinated by the processes of this once great industry. He had what amounted to an artist's interest in the various machines used, as his photography shows. Local people are typically purposeful and loyal, and for many of the steelmen the work they did, so tough and unremitting, was more than a job , more part of a team, always ready with a joke, for without a sense of humour the process would have been unbearable!

Ken was a member of the Outreach Team in the 1980s which produced publicity for the 1986 Garden Festival, and thoroughly enjoyed seeing the regeneration of the devastated site.

Turbo-blower house. Adamson No 4
and Richardsons Westgarth No 5.

Blast furnace turbo-blower house,
with site of coking plant 1968

Blast furnaces wrecking gang in 1950s.
This arduous job entailed removal of the old blast furnace lining prior to rebuild.

The overhaul of the English Electric turbo-blower in 1950.

The cooling pools.

Blast furnaces 1978.

Producer gas generators early 1900s. These produced carbon monoxide 'gas' as fuel for the melting shop, by passing steam through red hot coke.

Thre top pictures on these two facing pages are
one continuous panorama of the blast furnaces.

Jan 24th 1963. The big freeze-up. Blast
furnace cooling ponds frozen up.

The Racecourse colliery.

The turbine house.

Open hearth smelting furnaces in 1964 - built in 1886.

Eleven
IRON SMELTING
Some details from Les Hall and Mr Field

In the 1930s men tapped the furnaces and iron ran out into sand beds in front of each furnace, which had specially prepared runnels in them. When the iron was cold men went with double-handled hammers and smashed the iron into 'pigs'or lumps, which weighed about 150-200 lbs (70-90 Kg). These had to be man-handled into waiting railway wagons - at quite a height in the early days - lifted from the ground and stacked criss-cross. The men who performed this very arduous task were called 'pig lifters', and they heaved them across their knees as they lifted them. At some stage railway wagons at a lower level were used, and this eased the work a little.

A continuous casting plant was installed in 1942. This had a big conveyor belt made of iron moulds. There was a 40 ton ladle on a tilting machine and this poured the molten iron into these moulds, and then they moved uphill under atomised sprays. At the top they were solid red pigs, which 'clonked' down into water for a final cooling (the clonking noise could be heard all over the district and is remembered with affection by Potteries folk). This new machinery did away with the sandbeds and was a big improvement, as the earlier method was very slow because the sandbeds had to be prepared and took up a great deal of space. Also the men's work was much less arduous.

British ore was very low grade, so iron ore was imported, the best coming from rich deposits in Sweden and South Africa. Ore brought from Narvik, in Norway, came via Liverpool and Birkenhead Docks, and was transported in rail wagon loads to Shelton. It was taken to an ore crusher at the North Works and made into rubble size. This was fed in at the top of the blast furnace, having been taken up in a 'bell', a large bucket with a false bottom. Ore, coke and limestone (the fluxing agent to get rid of impurities) was fed into the furnace. The process down the furnace was slow. At the bottom was the molten metal, then slag, then the ore and coke coming in cold at the top. Blast through the bottom coke created heat.

There was a continual 'tapping off'of the slag, or it would have reached the bottom. It was put into a 20 ton tipper ladle which then went to be tipped at the slag heap. When this tipping occurred the sky lit up with a rosey glow as the 15 to 20 tons of molten slag poured forth, the top darkened surface giving way to red and then white hot slag beneath.

The iron out of the blast furnace was grey when cold. Cast iron from the early furnaces was very brittle, so a method called 'puddling'to make it stronger was found, which involved stirring a known quantity of slag into the molten iron, thus creating 'wrought iron', which was used in the making of railways and gates. Old cannons were made of very thick, solid and heavy cast iron.

Twelve
STEEL SMELTING

Shelton Bar was a market leader in North Staffordshire, being the first works to make steel successfully, where others had tried and failed. A new melting shop was built and four basic open-hearth furnaces installed to operate by the Siemens Martin process, the first steel being produced in 1888.

It is surprising when people refer to the history of Shelton Bar that they tend to concentrate on the blast furnaces and the iron making - which of course is where it all started - but they make less of the steel making, which is even more important and interesting. The open hearth production of steel was particularly exciting. One could see the whole process from start to finish, unlike the iron making when all that could be seen was a huge vertical furnace into which materials were placed and processed without visual contact; even the tapping was tame compared to the steel furnace workings.

Electricity had come to Shelton in 1908, and an electrically operated charger was installed in the melting shop (with a second one in 1920). Now the furnaces were charged by mechanical means. From 1888 to 1908 men had charged the furnaces by hand, throwing the scrap metal, pig iron and limestone into the furnaces. This meant coming right up to the furnace openings, and the heat was intense, so the work was very arduous.

As well as the charger a 40 ton electrically operated overhead ladle crane was installed, running the whole length of the melting shop. This had a tremendous effect on the steel smelting. Hot metal could be transferred from the blast furnace in a 20 ton ladle and poured directly into the steel furnace, thus eliminating the use of pig iron and reducing the smelting time. Having an overhead crane meant that all the raw materials, relining bricks, mortar etc. could be lifted into place onto the operating floor, which was 25 feet above ground level. Until this time everything had to be moved by men with wheelbarrows, first filled at ground level, pushed into a steam-hoist-operated lift at the north end, and then along the stage to the required furnace! When you realise that the melting shop was 500 feet long, and tons of raw materials were required to feed the furnaces, and add to these the many relining bricks, etc needed, you can perhaps realise what tremendous feats of human endeavour went into this early production of steel. Thank goodness for the discovery of electricity which so revolutionalised the material handling problems in industry, and lightened the load of many, including those early steel workers.

Each furnace produced 80 tons of steel per 24 hour 'heat'. However, Shelton operators had found a method to increase this by 20 tons, thus making 100 tons per 'heat'. They would build an aggregate dam wall on the three door sills, thus raising the molten metal level within the furnace! This was extremely warm work as the doors had to be raised whilst the building of the dam was done with shovels! When the molten metal was bubbling within the furnace there was always a danger that the dam might burst and flood the shop floor with white hot metal! It never did, so skilful were the operators, but there were many close squeaks.

A furnace went 28 to 32 heats before a complete reline, which took a week; therefore with five furnaces four were always in production. With care and fettling there were occasions when the five furnaces were producing. When a furnace was ready for tapping the steel would be bubbling and this would knock great holes in the inside brick lining of the furnace. When all the molten metal had left, the furnace men would 'fettle' (ie smooth off) these holes with aggregate grit. They had to go right up to the charging door and shovel it in, and were experts at directing it right into the holes. (Peter Cheeseman gives a good description of this in his notes on the Victoria Theatre's production of *Fight for Shelton Bar*)

Tapping an open hearth steel furnace was an exciting and very dangerous event. Four men stood ready, clad in moleskin shirts, ordinary trousers, clogs, cloth caps and wet towels around their necks and lower part of their faces - proper protective clothing for furnace operators did not arrive until the early 1950s! Two of the men stood in the firebrick lined chute which directed the white hot metal into the ladle at ground level some 20 feet below. The other men stood one on each side of the chute wall. A pneumatic drill was lowered on a chain from an overhead crane, and the men would direct the drill into the tap hole. The drill unit had specially designed arms fitted so that all the men could exert pressure. The tap hole was 9 inches in diameter and passed through the furnace steel structure and a 2 foot firebrick lining to the furnace bottom, which was designed to slope from all points to the hole. Prior to a new 'heat' the hole had been filled with a 'marl'plug, and rammed home; by the end of the heat it would be like a solid mass of concrete. This took some getting through and tremendous pressure was necessary to force the drill up and into the furnace. The 'tap' took from 15 to 30 minutes, and the men were so close to the furnace casing, and the heat and exertion so great, their wet towels round their necks and faces steamed! The only hand protection the men had was spats made of asbestos cloth, which covered the palms and underside of the fingers.

When the breakthrough came the white hot metal spurted through with terrific force, and the four men had to jump onto a small platform on either side of the chute and move VERY quickly up steps to the upper platform 5 feet above! One false slip and they would be caught up in the molten metal cascading into the ladle at ground level! This cascade of white hot metal was a wonderful sight, but even better was to come:

On the upper platform were pre-weighed minerals: carbon (anthracite in 7lb paper bags), ferro-silicon, ferro-manganese and sticks of aluminium. When the ladle was half full these were thrown or shovelled into the hot metal, being the essential ingredients to provide the required grade and quality of steel. When the minerals hit the molten metal they caused a chemical reaction which resulted in flames 20 to 30 feet into the air, and the ladle was enveloped in millions of red sparks!! It was like a volcanic eruption and a spectacle to behold. The first time Les witnessed this, as a fourteen year old, he was rooted to the spot in amazement, and he never tired of seeing the sight over and over again. Ever afterwards fireworks and bonfires meant nothing at all to him.

When the ladle was nearly full there would be a colour change in the metal coming from the furnace from white to red, and this indicated that all the steel had been withdrawn and only red hot molten slag remained. The operators then swung the chute over, for it had a central pivot axle, and directed the molten slag into a rough hole in the ground (5ft in diameter and 18" deep) where it formed when cold a sort of 'cow-pat' weighing between 5 and 7 tons. This was removed in a solid mass, taken to the basic slag works, smashed up, put in a ball mill and ground to a powder, to become 'basic slag fertiliser'.

Les said the memories of the old steel smelting shop would live with him for ever, and I guess there are many thousands of steelmen who would say the same. The charging, the pouring of the molten metal iron into the furnace, the taking of a sample in a 10ft long ladle hand operated into the boiling, white, bubbling metal; the tapping; the fettling, and last but not least the re-lining of the furnace, an art and craft in itself - for the bricklayers designed the roof, arches, flues and the sloping base to and around the tapping hole. He counted it a privilege to have seen and been a part of this passage of industrial history!

'Tapping the bear' - pig beds of sand.

Roy Brassington at the final lighting of the furnace.

Thirteen
CHILDHOOD MEMORIES OF SHELTON BAR

My own childhood memories mingle with thoughts of Shelton Bar, for my father was a painter there for as long as I can remember. I recall that he had a real respect for the management, and some of the big bosses, especially Mr Neville Rollason, for whom he did some work at his home during the war. Dad spent a week at his country home in Peplow, and while he was away our brave, strong mum was working night shifts at a munition factory, on a shell machine - which was really a man's job. One night there was an air-raid, and mother couldn't bear the thought of her three young daughters being alone at home, so she left the factory and began the three mile trudge to get back to us. In the pitch darkness she almost bumped into two men on firewatch duty and she was very scared, however she reached us safely, and I guess we were very relieved children although I can't remember it now.

Dad used to talk a great deal about the engines he painted at the works, and the crossing gates, which many will remember were situated at the bottom of Cobridge Road. He also worked frequently in Etruria Hall, for which building he had a great affection.

There was good companionship in the painters' shop, which was situated somewhere behind the canteen, on the Cobridge Road side of the works. I remember when I was ten we had a holiday in Blackpool with one of Dad's fellow painters and his wife. It must have been a good year, for it was the only time we ever stayed in a boarding house.

Dad was in charge of the sickness fund I remember, for which he collected every week. This was to help anyone who had to take time off sick. Les Hall said he must have been a member of the Welfare Committee. There was no such thing as sick pay in those days.

One particular Saturday morning will stay in my mind for ever. I was 15 and my sister 14, and we had to go down to the works to give our Dad some wonderful news: he had become the father of a son at last! I remember him striding across the big canteen toward us as we stood there, hardly able to contain the news till he got to us.

"Dad, it's a boy and Mum's all right!" I said.

"Eh, that's good in't eet, Jo?" he replied with beaming face.

Our Mother had had a rough time during her pregnancy at 38 years of age, but I knew she felt it all worth it to have a son at last. And all the family spoilt him!

As time went on Dad would bring wooden toys made on the works for our little brother. He would paint them in bright colours and bring them home. He made us laugh once when he told us about getting one off the works; the lodgeman at the crossing gates said to him,

"I ought to ask yer what yer've got under yer coat, Bill!"

Dad replied, "Thee wouldsna believe if a told thee!"

So his friend replied, "Go on then, try me!"

"It's a locomotive engine!"

"Get off with yer, yer silly bugger!" the man said and passed him through with a chuckle.

Life was hard and Dad had to work every hour he could to keep us all. This included Saturday and Sunday mornings, and even Christmas Day. One Christmas his friends must have persuaded him to go with them for a celebratory drink before going home for his Christmas dinner. It was 3 o'clock when he wobbled his way down the back yard, and my

Mother was furious. I can't remember the ensuing row, but it must have been a good one, for he was never late again! There's a picture by L.S. Lowry, called 'Father going home', which rather reminds me of the incident: it couldn't be our Dad though, because the man's sporting a trilby hat and carrying an umbrella..... however he is tipping backwards!

Years later when I was a student in college, a Dutchman I had met at a conference came to stay with us for a weekend. Since he was interested in the steelworks Dad arranged to take us on a visit there. It was fascinating, but my most abiding memory of the visit is of the Dutchman trying to make sense of what the blastfurnaceman was telling him: even I could barely understand his pottery dialect. (The expression double dutch springs to my mind!)

My Father retired from Shelton Bar in 1971 when he was 65.

My father, William Lakin, left with specs, Mr Titley, centre, Frank ----, far right, and other painters.

C 1920.

Early 1900s excavations for No 1 blast furnace.

Molten steel 'teeming' into a steel ladle. By Alf Wakefield.

Fourteen
THE WELFARE FUND

There were many responsible people on the Welfare Committee throughout the works. The Company stopped 1d (penny) per week off each employee which went into the Welfare Fund. The Committee would meet regularly in the canteen, after working hours, unpaid, to request the Secretary (a member of the Wages Staff, again voluntary and unpaid) for payment to those whom they considered qualified for help. The payment for four weeks sickness was £1, and for every following week £1. If a man had to give up his job due to ill health he was paid a one off payment of £5.

If a man was killed on the works his dependents were paid a one off payment of £5, plus a collection made throughout the works. Though the payments were small they were much appreciated. The Welfare Fund paid the cost of the children's parties (workers'children only) which were a great event in the week before Christmas, and organised by Committee members. But I can't ever remember any of our family going to one of these.

The Welfare Fund operated until the works closed, with very little change in the rules. Les received £1 in 1957, when he was off work for 5 weeks due to having an operation in Longton Cottage Hospital. After the war the Fund provided monies for equipment required for the cricket, bowls and football clubs. It is interesting to note that before the National Health Service came into being each employee was also stopped 1d to which was added 1d per employee paid by the firm, and this money went to the North Staffs Royal Infirmary to ensure free hospital treatment for workers and their dependents. A welfare stoppage still operated in the 1990s at the works and monies were paid out to various charities.

No-one minded the stopping of 2d from their wages, man and boy alike, although in pre-war days this was a lot.... but there was no income tax in those days for these workers, because no one earned enough to qualify!

Removing the pigs from the sand beds.

Fifteen
WARTIME BLACKOUT AT SHELTON BAR

Memories of wartime are still vivid for people who worked at Shelton Bar during the war. Les Hall told me about the works efforts at camouflage. Hiding from the German bombers was really not a great problem as all the iron and steel smelting and rolling mills were in enclosed buildings of necessity. Certain buildings had open sides and gable ends and these were sheeted up, leaving a gap of 18" for floor level ventilation. All the roofs had louvred ventilators and these were 'lap-louvred' to prevent glare during tapping and furnace door opening. The only parts of the plant open to the elements, the coke ovens and gas producing plant (down the west side of the steel melting shop), were covered by galvanised sheets on scaffolding pole frames. The additional sheeting made working conditions grim. The heat, especially during the summer, was unbearable, but in true Shelton fashion the men bore it all with a shrug of the shoulders. Lighting outside afforded no problem - there was none anyway!

Air raid shelters were put down throughout the works, but were never used, for the men said that if they went to the shelters when the sirens sounded they would have had to damp down the furnaces, and this was something that they could not achieve 'at the drop of a hat'. To damp down a furnace there had to be co-ordination with gas producers, boilers, turbo blowers, power station etc, and it took very 'delicate' arranging! The coking plant likewise could not be shut down; it was absolutely essential, to keep the ovens in fine fettle - to work flat out. As soon as the coke was pushed out, the oven had to be charged with slag without delay, otherwise the oven would distort and that would have been disastrous.

The only section of the works that could be shut down immediately were the two rolling mills (18" and 32"), but this would mean the loss of rolled and finished steel production, which was so needed. The men decided to carry on working as normal. Fortunately the works were never hit by bombs, and full production was maintained throughout the war.

Iron and steel making has to take place under cover because molten iron and steel does not mix with water. If water is poured onto molten metal it becomes volatile, turning quickly to steam and causing instant explosion; of course it is extremely dangerous. In the 1970s there was a shocking accident at the Scunthorpe Works when a loco was transporting a ladle of molten iron from the blast furnaces to the steel melting shop. Since it was a nice day no lid was fitted. En route there was a fractured overhead water pipe directly over the railway line, and as the ladle passed under this, water fell onto the molten metal. A mighty explosion ensued in which the loco driver and a shunter riding on the footplate were killed, and three men at work in the vicinity were also injured. Questions asked at the inquest were:

Were the blast furnace staff informed about the water pipe fracture?
Did the loco driver not see the fracture and water pouring onto the railway line?
Why was the line not closed to traffic? .....

And most importantly:

Had it been explained to the loco driver, and other workers why in wet weather a ladle lid must be fitted to a ladle before leaving the blast furnace area?'

This all goes to prove how much there was to learn for a prospective iron and steel worker. Knowledge, good sense and caution were as necessary as the strength to do it!

Sixteen
THE KALDO STEEL MAKING PLANT

The Kaldo pneumatic steel making process was selected as being the most suitable for the production of steel from high phosphorous hot metal with a usage of up to 40% of scrap. The process provided a precise control over steel analysis and casting temperatures essential for continuous casting.

The Shelton installation was housed in a building 460 feet long by 180 feet wide and 115 feet high, divided into two bays at the south end and three at the north. The plant consisted of two Kaldo stands with four interchangeable 55 ton refractory lined vessels, thus enabling continuous working of two vessels with two being relined. A vessel could be changed in about two hours by joining together two 140 ton cranes and driving them as one unit.

The Kaldo refractory lined vessel was 20 feet high with a diameter of 14 feet. Fitted on the outer shell were two cast iron rings, and the vessel was placed on a tilting frame, the two rings resting on four rollers each driven by a 100 h.p. motor and capable of rotating the vessel at 40 r.p.m. In the operating position the vessel lay at 18" to the horizontal. The mouth was covered by a swinging frame which, in addition to collecting all the fume from the process, also carried the water cooled oxygen lance. The oxygen was piped to six storage cylinders outside the Kaldo building, suppied from a plant situated on the perimeter of the works.

The fume collected in the hood was passed through dry electrostatic precipitations and cleaned before being released into the air. The iron oxide in the fume was pelletised on withdrawal from the cleaners and delivered to the blast furnace department sinter plant.

A phosphoric slag was removed from the Kaldo by pouring into a diesel driven slag ladle. This slag was tipped from the ladle into lagoons outside the steel plant building and then removed and transported to the basic slag plant.

The steel was tapped into a 55 ton ladle which was transferred on an electric driven car to the casting plant.

The time taken from the charging of the vessel with iron and scrap etc. and pouring the steel produced was approximately 1 hour.

Molten iron was delivered to the plant from the blast furnaces half a mile away and stored in a 1,000 ton mixer. The correct weight of iron was poured from the mixer as required into a transfer ladle standing on a load cell weighbridge. This ladle was then taken to the Kaldo by one of the 140 ton cranes and the hot metal poured into the vessel.

Scrap was delivered to the plant in rail wagons and loaded direct onto scrap cars standing on load cell weighbridges. The two scrap cars were propelled by diesel hydraulic drive, each car having four hydraulically tipped boxes. The scrap was loaded into these boxes by two magnet cranes.

Additions used in the process were stored in high level bunkers above each Kaldo. Below each set of bunkers was a five department larry car which was fed by vibrating feeders from the bunkers. The feeder and weighing equipment were remotely controlled from the Kaldo pulpit, the required weights of material being weighed out and discharged into the Kaldo via a chute.

Seventeen
MORE MEMORIES FROM LES

Les and Con Hall moved to Basford in 1956, mainly to be close to the works - within walking distance. On dark winter's nights, sometimes when returning home, Les would stand on the brow of Basford Bank and look down the Etruria valley. Below lay a black smoking 'pit', here and there glowing red, and prickling with hundreds of lights: Etruria, where the great Josiah Wedgwood had made his home and built his factory! Now it was gone, moved to the green fields of Barlaston, clean and fresh, with no bottle ovens, but all electric and modern. Les would stare down into that pit of human endeavour, at the black buildings, some flickering with light from within, as a river of liquid gold flowed through them. Clouds of steam and smoke drifted across the shadowy vale, rosey steam lit from fires below.

There was a continuous hollow rushing sound, broken by clanks of shunting and metal crashing against metal. A steam engine would rise up suddenly on a slag mound towing a ladle of molten slag, black against red, like a slide moving backwards and forwards. The whole pit seemed to breathe as it worked. Though it was only 6 p.m. it was extremely dark, and naked lights on gantries and signals glittered all over Etruria. Suddenly a deep orange glow would spread across the sky, swallowing other reds in its brightness. It was a reflection of what he couldn't see, but knew was there, a forty foot slab of red hot coke, packed solid and pulsing, sliding into the night air, pushed from the coke ovens of the coking plant. As the glow diminished to darkness the air was again filled with a sudden red hot blast, as the steam engine discharged its 10 tons of molten slag from the ladle.

Etruria was like a pit of loathing, a very hell of malodorous, malevolent dust and noxious powders! No wonder the Potteries had such a foul reputation! The sulphurous atmosphere of all the furnace area brought tears to the eyes and stinging to the nose and throat. Swirling, acrid, yellow smoke from the gas producers enveloped the melting shop with its smell of rotten eggs. The foul smell within the rolling mills was similar to open sewage, and was due to polluted canal water and the water that came from 'Lady's Well' being used to cool the production rolls. 'Lady's Well' was an old worked out marl pit on the Hanley side of the Top Works, near to Century Street. Into this flowed street drainage and storm water from Hanley, and this being Shelton Bar's land, provided a ready and free water supply. They pumped this into the mills for cooling purposes, but the smell was vile, especially in the summer!

Constant emissions of hot steam provided a clammy atmosphere and a smell of unwashed bodies. If you worked in the coking plant you carried home a smell of creosote and tar on your clothes. Con always knew when Les had been there and made him change his clothes in the porch before he went into the house! Members of the public sometimes objected to sitting next to Shelton Bar men on public transport, even writing to the 'Evening Sentinel' about their dirty, evil smelling clothes. In the early days there were no clothes lockers or washing facilities, and the men carried home with them whatever they had picked up during their shift.

The dirt and dust of a great industry (red ore dust, black coal dust, grey coke dust and white brick dust) rose up above the works, driven by the heat, to form a great cloud hundreds of feet above the valley! Then, driven by the prevailing winds and losing its heat support, it dropped on all the surrounding areas, Basford, Hartshill, Wolstanton, Porthill and Cobridge. How well I remember the soot strewn window sills and black-smocked washing of our childhood days! The old Shelton Bar would never have passed the Clean Air Act stipulations! In Etruria Park, where tennis and bowls were played, when the wind came from the south and a 'charging slip' occurred, the players would see a huge black cloud approaching. Then they would abandon their game and beat a hasty retreat into the pavilion, where they would stay for 15 minutes or so until the cloud had passed over. Les and Con played tennis for Etruria Park in the Stoke Parks' League, and he described the sudden breaks in play as 'frustrating'! When their game was over the new match balls would be dark grey in colour.

In spite of all the unpleasant aspects of life in living or working in Etruria, everyone still speaks of the place with real affection. I have yet to meet an Etruscan who complains about the old life!

Gas cleaning plant, June 1978. The tall stack was for burning off gas.

British Steel production at Shelton.
(Courtesy of British Steel)

Below:
Last cast, No. 4 blast furnace, June
22nd 1978.

Eighteen
LATER YEARS AT SHELTON BAR: Les Hall's Memories

"Old fashioned apprenticeships cannot be beaten", said Les, and most skilled workers would agree with this. Today's industrialists and educators are realising it again too. He learnt a great amount from the iron and steel workers of days gone by, in fact all the rudiments of the industry. As a messenger boy he saw all the different processes and was encouraged to ask questions, politely of course; also he studied hard at night school. He remembered from the 1930s talking to the men who worked on the sand beds where the molten iron ran. He asked them if their feet got burnt, because they got quite close to the hot metal. They assured him that they didn't, because of their clogs and the sand which protected them. "You know how kids bury their dad in the sand on holiday? Well, he stays cool, 'cos the sand insulates him."

Les remembered this many years later when he advised that electricity cables should be underground, imbedded in sand, and not constructed high up in the mills, but his boss would not agree. Afterwards there were many problems, as heat rises, and the cables frequently caught fire. During the early planning for the Kaldo and Concast continuous casting plant it was realised that there was insufficient ground space for the whole set up, so only 11 instead 14 concast machines were installed, shortage of money being another reason. Each machine had to have a motor generator, and the contractor room holding these ran the length of the mill, built high up above the machines. The whole building had to be strengthened to take the weight. This was not very satisfactory and there were frequent fires - for example, if a ladle bottom dropped out 40 tons of molten metal would spew out onto the floor below, the heat rose and cables would be set on fire!

The heat and noise were terrific, but in those days no ear muffs were worn. In fact the engineers had to be listening all the time for any change in the sound of the machines running, as this could indicate a fault. It was also necessary from a safety point of view. All over the works big notices read: STOP! LOOK! LISTEN!

These were especially important on the old works, when steam locomotives were used to move the ladles of molten metal. This would sometimes slop out throwing sparks everywhere and was very dangerous. Slag was transported to the slag heaps in this way, and when they had deposited their loads the locos were returned to the Etruria sidings by gradient, ie on the down slope and with no other locomotion - and these unmanned locos were the cause of more deaths than any other process. The slag ladles took 10-15 tons at a time, and lime was added to stop the slag sticking to the ladle. The molten metal ladles took 40 tons at a time and were brick lined to prevent the metal sticking.

Les had to rely on his hearing for his work, but he also had to be able to 'switch off' in order to concentrate on important matters in hand. The noise was awesome, and, as for many of the workers, his hearing became impaired in later years.

There had to be two lifts for the people who needed to go up and down the continuous casting plant. One, an Otis, was fine, but the second, a Keathley lift, was far from satisfactory, and unsuitable for a steelworks. Shelton had to have it to save funds. And it was not until 1972 that Les got his way with the electric cables. They were put underground, imbedded in sand and covered with cement and a metal sheeting. From then on they had no further trouble.

Mrs Margaret Ellen, production controller - very few ladies have reached such a status in heavy manufacturing.

Nineteen
PREMONITION... A TRUE AND MOVING STORY
by the late Roy Brassington

Mr. Roy Brassington was foreman bricklayer on the blast furnaces, and he wrote a very interesting *History of Staffordshire Iron Making over 18 Hundred Years*. His final words in this are striking not only because he foresaw what would happen in later years in the steel industry, but also for the fascinating industrial language he uses. For outsiders like myself it is strange, baffling, even amusing:

Foundry iron, forge iron and cylinder iron were produced and also 90 puddling furnaces and 8 rolling mills were supplying structural sections and more particularly a very high quality rail, much in demand by local and national railroads. This speciality continued to be a great asset until the introduction of the Kaldo process just prior to nationalisation, when the quality of steel produced proved unacceptable to the railroad. There are now three furnaces, two in blast and one in reserve, all burdened by sinter and scrap, producing 6,000 tons per week if supplies are available. The higher production is mainly the result of using sinter, which is ore and coke fines and flue dust and mill scale, graded, mixed and dead burned. The burning process clinkers the fines and drives off the volatiles, thus reducing the bulk of the material and increasing the yield by as much as 25 per cent.

The remaining chapters of the Shelton saga have yet to unfold, but the end of iron and steel making there, after 250 years, is imminent!

Now the story (I believe written about 1975)

I am a Staff Foreman Bricklayer engaged on the maintenance and repair of Blast Furnaces and Ancillary Plant in the Midlands Steelworks of the B.S.C. I have held this position for more than thirty years, during which time I have been accustomed to being on call all hours of the day and night and almost any day of the year. So urgent are some calls that the Works Security Police have interrupted a Church service to contact me, and I have frequently worked forty hours without respite.

During my service I have been ably supported and served by my deputy, George Woods, who had worked with me from the time of his discharge from the army. His willingness was matched only by his unfailing cheerfulness, and many varied experiences had forged a very deep bond between us.

Unfortunately, George's health deteriorated severely during the past 15 years, mainly through rheumatoid arthritis, which slowly but inexorably locked his joints, commencing with his fingers, then wrists and eventually his feet, knees and hips.

Despite a series of operations, including replacement of his hip joints, he repeatedly returned to work and struggled on as best he could, never shirking any duty and remaining as cheerful as ever. Along with his main infirmity, George also suffered from ulcers, haemorroids, and at one period a double hernia. In reply to enquiries about his health, George invariably replied, *"You name it, I've got it!"*

Towards the middle of last year his infirmities increased to such an extent that I had to insist on him taking things more easily, and I had him engaged mainly on clerical duties and purely supervisory work, but he still retained his cheerfulness and banter and never complained.

The Blast Furnace Plant could well have the same slogan as the wartime Windmill Theatre, namely "We never close", therefore arrangements had to be put in hand to cover staffing in our department over the Christmas period, for work would continue without interruption, holiday or no. I agreed to work Christmas Day and Boxing Day, 1974, so that George could have Christmas at home, for he was a dedicated family man and looked forward to meeting as many members of the family as possible. In return George would cover me on New year's Eve and New Year's Day.

This arrangement was duly carried out, and I settled myself down on New Year's Eve (with a bottle of whiskey) to watch the festivities on television, and as is our custom, I let the Old Year out and the New Year in at Midnight. My wife had retired to bed before midnight and I had told her that I would sleep in the second bedroom so as not to disturb her when I eventually came to bed.

This would be at approximately 2.30am and I was rapidly asleep, but very disturbed, and I began to dream vividly that George had come to tell me that he could no longer perform even the light duties that I had put him on. As I pleaded with him to try to continue, my wife awakened me to tell me that the time was 5.30 a.m. and the Works Police were at the door asking for me.

As I dressed I told her of my dream and also that I feared that it was about to be fulfilled.

This proved correct; the Police told me that George had had a seizure during the night and had been rushed to the hospital, where he had gone into the Intensive Care Unit and therefore I should have to go to work that morning.

George sank into a coma and passed away five days later, never fully recovering consciousness.

I might add that I rarely dream, and even more rarely remember a dream, but this experience was so vivid and the timing so uncanny that I am convinced that this was a message from George transmitted to me by some means beyond my comprehension.

Georgie Wood and Roland Marks, blast furnace bricklayers' charge-hand and blast furnace manager respectively. Roland's father was head roller of the 18 inch Mill.

Alf Wakefield with some of his pictures

Below:
Union gathering in the 1960s to present Wedgwood bowl to Sir David Davies, Gen. Sec. of Iron and Trades Confederation.
Ted Smith second from right, Jim Wakelin, blast furnace manager, far left.

Twenty
THE STORY OF ALF WAKEFIELD
Electrician and Artist Extraordinaire

Born in Garibaldi Street, Etruria, in 1926, Alf Wakefield is a true Etruscan, for he spent all his childhood in the village, and most of his working life at Shelton Bar Iron, Steel and Coal Works. He was a maintenance electrician, getting to know every aspect of the works, and is a mine of information!

Much of his leisure time went and still goes in recording its remarkable views in oils on canvas. From the earliest age Alf was an acute observer of everything that went on in the village; and he became very familiar with the works layout, because he used to take his Grandfather's 'snapping' (food and drink) onto the works for him, where the latter was a mill foreman. Though Alf did not begin drawing or painting until the 1940s, he had an artist's eye for detail from the very beginning and still today has the benefit of a vivid memory.

Through his work Alf got to know many of the workmen on the 'Bar' and was a member of the Welfare Committee in later years. Amongst his dearest friends, he and his wife Kath numbered the sons of the Steele family, Jack, Edgar and Wilf, who along with their two sisters were actually born on the works, in the Armoury Cottages! These had been built in the previous century and were situated, as many older workers will remember, to the back, right of Etruria Hall. Jack, the eldest son, followed his Father as electrical foreman for the whole works, and he received the BEM for his services to the firm. Alf recalls how Edgar was once asked by the boss, 'walking the works', how long he had been there.

Jack Steel receiving his BEM. Other Shelton men to be honoured include Mr Ralph Evans, OBE, chief works engineer and Charles Myatt, BEM, a foreman bricklayer.

"Sixty-five years!" he replied. *"Impossible!"* said the boss. Edgar explained then that he had been born there - and no one could have a better record than that.

Alf Wakefield who became shift foreman for all electrical work.

Right: Cedric Wrench (left), whose father was a loco driver, seen here with Alf and an electrical motor being repaired.

Below:
One of Alf's fine industrial pictures, 'Above pithead scene at Cannock'. Alf was a Bevin Boy miner in the War.

When the Steeles had gone to live in the big white house in Forge Lane, the Armoury Cottages were taken over by the basic slag works, for storing the bags of basic slag in. Two women, one named Daisy, were employed to stamp and move the heavy bags before they were carted away.

Memories of old Etruria came flooding back to Alf. There was old Mrs Lockett (probably not as old as he remembered her as a little boy) in her long black skirt and head shawl, who sold milk from churns which she wheeled on their rims down the road. Later in the day she would be selling coal from an old handcart. Her son, Harry, worked at Shelton Bar.

Alf (and presumably Harry too!) remembered the girls of the village with their luscious, long hair, usually plaited and done up in a 'bun'. It was woe betide any girl who had her hair 'bobbed' without first asking her father's permission, for fathers ruled the roost! There was a 'muffin man' who came round the village with a tray piled high with items of pottery for sale, ('muffin' is the pottery word for a small round plate). Alf says he can still hear the man's bell going 'ding-a-ling-a-ling' to advertise his wares. He recalled how hard it was in those days to make ends meet, and told of his amazement when he saw four Scotsmen in full regalia standing on a street corner in the village playing their bagpipes: they were busking as he realises now, but to a little Etruria lad it was a completely alien scene.

Alf was only four when his Father, a porter at Stoke Station, died. This meant that he, his little Brother and his Mum had to find fresh lodgings. Mrs Wakefield was lucky to find these, and work too, in Lucy McCabe's dress shop on the main road, Lord Street, as it was then called. She helped in the shop and they had the bedroom above, where the little boys, left to their own devices, spent much time at the window watching everything that went on in the village.

Alf learnt a great deal about the Etruscan way of life, and remembers with glee all the comings and goings at the butcher's shop, situated further down the street and opposite, on the corner of Forge Lane. The butchers, named Palmer, slaughtered their own beasts, and the little boys loved to watch the sheep and cows being herded from the railway station down the cobbled street to the shop, some coming from Newcastle market too. The butchers did a marvellous trade, especially with the rich people from Hanley and the Westlands, who passed through the village. Christmas time was especially exciting, for there would be lines of turkeys hanging up outside the shop, and rows of pigs' heads with oranges in their mouths in the window! One can imagine the fascination of the little boys, with their noses pressed to the window pane! Little of this festive fare found its way onto Etruscan tables of course, except for a boiling fowl if folk were lucky, or a piece of pork.

Further down the village, in-between the potworks and the parts of the steel works near to Etruria Hall, there was an area of spare ground called 'The Pool Fields', which was gradually being filled in with pottery waste. Here young men would gather to gamble at 'pitch-penny', but they were always on their guard, for the police often raided. It was here that the works cricket pitch would eventually be sited. Alf recalled a sad memory of the Tew family, who had two sons working on the Bar when he was a little boy. One went home to fetch his tea and sugar which he had forgotten: on his way back he tried to skate across the frozen pool, fell through the ice and was drowned.

He remembered the 'boatees' too, who plied the canal with their barges laden with materials for the various factories nearby. They used to send their childen to the local Etruria School in clogs or bare feet, and the teacher would appeal often for old socks and shoes for these poor kids.

When Alf went to school he was treated as an oddity because he was left handed, and put into a 'C' class. He knew even then that it was unjust, and he was sad that he was not allowed to draw or paint, for it was something he wanted to do very badly. In later years he was fired with a fierce determination to prove himself - I believe this is one of the things which have made his paintings unique! As he says himself, every stroke of the brush is HIM completely, for he never had an hour's art lesson in his life!

When Alf was 14 he should have had a job at Shelton Bar, which his Grandfather was getting for him. Unfortunately, the latter died of a heart attack on the works, during the first air raid that took place over Etruria in 1940. Workmates brought the body home, and the 14 year old lad had the ordeal of helping to lay his grandfather out!

Alf became apprenticed to the Staffs Potteries Water Board, where his Foreman, George Boffey, told him a great deal about the young Reginald Mitchell, of 'Spitfire' fame, who had been apprenticed under him at his previous job with 'Kirk and Stewart'. Later Alf became a 'Bevin Boy' at Chatterley Whitfield Colliery - boys of 14 drafted into the mines to help the war effort, by order of the Minister of National Defence and Employment, Mr Ernest Bevin.

Work at Shelton Bar began for Alf in 1947, when the firm employed some 10,000 people, having five coal mines at the time. Much earlier, at the tender age of eleven, Alf had been allowed to drive a large machine on the Bar (unofficially of course!), namely the ingot charger in the 32" mill, by the driver, Mr Adlington. In later years this machine became one of the subjects for Alf's brush! When Alf began to work at Shelton Bar he formed part of a team which carried out electrical repairs all over the works from Shelton's own central electrical workshop.

One of his earliest jobs was to repair flexes on the magnets which worked the pig conveyor belt or trolley lines, that had replaced the old pig bed system in the early 1940s. These had to be kept going whatever the weather and steam rose from them constantly. The big boss at the time was Mr George Goodwin, a fine man who spoke his mind, sometimes in florid language, and knew his men. He encouraged development of initiative and character, and there are many tales of devotion and co-operation to be told, for the working environment was harsh and dangerous.

Alf recalled a night when there was a bad storm and lightning struck the sinter plant. Everything went wrong and he did four and a half hours overtime, using a great bag full of fuses, from the tiniest to big 8" ones, to repair the damage. It was an eerie experience going home to Basford afterwards as the lightning continued to hit wires and make them 'ping' all the way.

He progressed in his work and became chargehand and later foreman in electrical maintenance for all the cranes on the works. Later on the system changed, and he became foreman on his shift, responsible for the whole works, so the workload was heavy and varied. Alf found it a challenge and revelled in it. He worked nine consecutive Christmas Days on the afternoon shift (2.00-10.00pm) - so he enjoyed a happy time with his wife and family before going on duty.

One particularly frightening incident in his early days, also had its funny side. He and a rather slow moving mate were called to some faulty switch gear in the Blast Furnace Sub-station. This was a long room with several decks of switches along each side, and only one exit. Since he wasn't sure where the fault lay, Alf asked his mate to turn off three of the switches: One! Two, and on the third there was a terrific bang! His mate was out through the door 'like greased lighning', as a chain reaction set up and all the switches blew up one after another. By now Alf was curled up in a corner, hands over head, in fear of his life. The place was filled with flames, smoke and noise! When he emerged eventually from the door, shaken but unharmed, it was to be told that his assistant had fainted on the road, and the whole works had come to a standstill! After this Alf was sent home for the rest of the shift, especially as he had been feeling unwell before the incident with a tummy bug. Following this blow-up Les Hall had to design a whole new sub-station!

Another story is even more dramatic and had a very sad ending, and poignant for myself as I discovered soon afterwards. A 55 year old electrician, who had worked for the firm for 35 years, had been called to deal with a fault at the top of the largest blast furnace. It was a Sunday and 7.20am. When no word had been heard from him for 20 minutes - the allotted time to call in and report - it was realised that something was amiss, so Alf raced up to the top of the furnace to investigate. He circled round the dark, covered way at the top of the furnace twice, and emerged, having found nothing, spluttering and rubbery legged from the fumes. He called for more help and chargehand, George Lee, sent up a young man named Roy Wood. Alf said he would go in once again, and that if he yelled, Roy was to race in to him immediately. Once more he circled round the furnace top and this time stumbled over the unconscious man. He yelled and Roy rushed in, and the two managed to drag the victim into the open air. Sadly the man was pronounced dead when taken to the ambulance room. When I was talking to my daughter-in-law a few days later about Alf, she asked me if he had mentioned anyone named Len Jones? It was the name of the victim, her grandfather, and father of one of my own school friends!

Alf was gassed and both men needed hospital treatment. Though barely 'with it', Alf remembered remonstrating with the sister when she told him to lie on a nice clean bed in his filthy clothes, and she almost threw him onto it! He was given oxygen and allowed home after several hours. For the next month he suffered with a terrible headache. The next two days should have been his normal rest days, but on Monday morning he received a call from the works to go in and take over Mr Jones's job!! This piece of information astounded me, and made me realise how different things were then, in the 1950s, compared to today's more enlighened ways! It gives you some idea of the man's dedication!

Stringent new safety rules at the blast furnaces were brought into being following the tragedy, including the wearing of masks and isolating of the furnace - that is turning off the blast - before electricians could attend to any repairs up there. Two years later the rescuers were awarded medals for their bravery by their Works Union.

Alf gave an interesting postscript to the story. When his boss, the outspoken Mr. Goodwin, saw him back at work so soon, he said,

"What the b... h... are you doing here?"

Mr Goodwin was accompanied that day by Mr V. H. Herbert, Managing Director from Summers, to whom he said, *"In the old days I would have sent him to bury his head in the earth at 'Longport Sidings'!"*

"Whatever for?" asked Mr. Herbert.

"Mother Nature would have got rid of the gas from his lungs in a couple of hours!" he replied. He was quite serious! Mr Goodwin was an expert in the field of metallurgy and a chemist in his own right.

It was with particular feeling that Alf recalled a young man he had known at Shelton Bar in the 1940s, a happy-go-lucky chap, who was an armature winder. During the war he served as a bomb aimer in the R.A.F. and made 83 sorties over enemy territory. When he returned he was a changed man, quiet and nervy. However he settled down to his job again, and was responsible for setting up the works football club and probably the cricket as well. In time he married and had two children and then emigrated to Australia. There apparently things did not go well - he actually killed his wife and served a long prison sentence! Years later Alf was amazed to see this man walking through Stoke. He stopped him to have a word with him, and the man asked about Shelton and whether the football teams were still playing. About eighteen months later Alf was greatly saddened to hear that this old workmate's body had been found on the railway lines at Etruria. He felt certain that it was the trauma of the young man's war experiences which had ruined his life.

Alf Wakefield's first attempts at art were in the 1940s, when he began to make pencil copies of portraits of famous people. The very first was of General Montgomery, copied from the front of The Radio Times, and it was such a good likeness that he was encouraged to continue. Afterwards came pen and ink studies aand all kinds of experiments in other media. He ventured boldly into oils, completely untutored, and as he dabbled he grew in confidence. His excellent memory and attention to detail always stood him in good stead. One of his early successes was a marvellous picture of the Houses of Parliament, which he took from a jigsaw puzzle! Then he began to paint scenes of the countryside, towns, canals, and railways, as well as pit-heads and potworks. However, his major interest and indeed obsession has always been with the steelworks, where he worked with such zeal and had such knowledge of all the complicated machinery and layout of the works.

To this day Alf Wakefield continues his 'involvement' with Shelton Bar and all its workers, and his enthusiasm as an artist is unabated. I think of him as the Potteries 'Lowry', and his work should be cherished as such. However, he is different from the Salford artist in two major ways: Alf was never an art student, (Lowry remained one all his days), but a steel worker who was constantly on the scene of his art; and secondly, the people in his pictures are not a hurrying, unidentifiable crowd, going anonymously on their way to earn their living, but people with names and characters, and specific jobs to do.

Alf Wakefield's pictures provide a unique record of the mighty industry which served its country and the world for over a century and a half, and today is facing a sad demise at the hands of the Dutch Hoogovens Firm which took over the remnants of Shelton Bar only a few months ago. Hearts go out not only to all the people who face unemployment, but to the fine iron and steel workers of the past who watch this sad ending.

Alf's art gives us a vision of people working in a tough and dangerous environment, now gone for ever. We should treasure it as part of our local and national heritage.

Twenty-one
FAMILIES AT SHELTON BAR - THE DUNN-ALLEN FAMILY

One Sunday in the 1990s on a guided tour of Etruria Hall I was fortunate to meet a lady who had lived most of her life and raised her family in the village of Etruria. She was accompanied by her eldest son, Kevin, who had worked on Shelton Bar for a while, and his wife. They were willing to talk about their life in this historic village, so it was a pleasure to meet them at a later date to hear their story. Mrs Hilda Dunn (née Allen) and her children had an astounding family tradition of working for the Bar. Their ancestors and relatives had totalled 575 years of service to the company!

Hilda Allen married John Stanley Dunn, uniting an amazing dynasty of Shelton Bar workers. Mr Dunn worked at Shelton Bar from the age of 14, until he died of a heart attack in 1974, as a fitter and a sinter plant worker. Hilda's youngest son, Stephen, is still working there today, near to completing his 30 years. It was a natural progession for youngsters born and bred in Etruria to seek employment at either the Wedgwood Potworks or the Shelton Iron and Steel Works. The elder brother, Kevin, had worked on the Bar from the age of 15 to 22, and then moved on to a career in lecturing. Stephen worked as a welder and boilermaker before becoming a maintenance worker. Their sister, Pauline, also worked in the Etruria Hall offices for 13 years.

When Kevin joined the firm after school he worked for 12 months in the template shop, and then went on to the construction department. Later he worked in one of the drawing offices in an annexe to the Hall. His uncle Bill was a rivet supporter in charge of a gang, and Kevin used to visit him in the 'Top Shop', and watch the riveter gangs at work. There were five furnaces for warming up the rivets, which were thrown down the shop with the shout 'rivets up!' by an apprentice to a catcher. The throwing was a tough, exhausting job, while the catcher just seemed to sit and catch.... he must have done other things too though Kevin didn't say what. He tried holding a rivet gun, which he said was massive, immensely heavy and made a terrible noise! I can imagine he was just as impressed as the young Les Hall had been in his early days there.

Kevin told me about the large number of cats on the site. These were necessary to deal with the vermin, especially at the 'Bottom End' (railway end) where there were big rats. He laughed as he remembered having to take a sick cat, a fierce, hissing ginger tom, to the surgery. His boss said, *"Take eet on yer bike, Eet wunner 'urt yer, an' sister'll give eet sumthin' to make eet better!"* As he rode off clutching the cat to him it dug its claws into his leather jacket, and when he arrived at the 'control room' the nurse told him to hold it down on the bench. She approached with the biggest hyperdermic needle the lad had ever seen, and rammed it forthwith into the cat's backside. The animal shrieked, sprang two feet in to the air out of his grasp and fled! It disappeared for a fortnight and then turned up again fighting fit!

Kevin also had memories of visiting the surgery on his own behalf, when he was afflicted with large boils on his neck, probably due to working in the atmosphere of the furnace presses. There was no messing he said - just a quick slit of the knife and plasters slapped on, as the sister turned her attention to another patient, newly arrived with what looked like half his thumb hanging off - the man said he had been putting a chock under a wheel of a loco! *"The loco backed onto me thumb!"* he said. *"That'll have to come off!"* said the sister, and Kevin thought she meant the thumb! But it was only the thumb nail, which she whipped off quickly without any fuss.... one can imagine the young man's shudder! But the workmen were used to such treatment.

Great Grandfather Dunn started work at Shelton Bar at the tender age of eight, in 1886. He grew up to become one of the drivers of the well known works' engine 'Cornist', though he had to stand on a box to do it because he was so small in stature! There was a tale of a driver being underneath the loco doing some oiling, when the fireman, all unaware, began moving it to another stand. When the loco stopped, out walked the driver swearing and sweating - he had been clinging onto the stretcher bars under the engine. Kevin wasn't sure whether the driver had been his great grandad or another driver.

He remembered as a small boy being sent by his grandmother to take his grandad's breakfast onto the works, a pot with a lid on it, containing beer, into which his grandad dunked his toast and ate it! His other grandad, Jack Dunn, served the firm as a crane driver, and was killed when his crane fell on top of him.

When I spoke to Stephen Dunn in 1998, he said that fewer and fewer men were being used to run the works, as the technology continued to improve. At that time efforts were being made to reduce the noise from the works, for the benefit of local people. I was surprised to hear that about 1,000 people from outside were engaged in some form of service to the works, in regard to maintenance, electrical and engineering matters for example; and I suppose that would include such people as hauliers too. Recently I learnt that a hire firm for lorries, diggers and other such equipment, had been working for Shelton Bar since 1947.

A study of the Dunn-Allen family tree will give readers some idea of the range of jobs and span of time this family gave to earning their living at the Shelton Bar site.

Kevin has some funny tales to tell about his early years in Etruria. He recalls the constant noise of hooters and buzzers, both from the steelworks and the potbank. When you add to them the noises from the nearby railway, the clanking of the iron, the constant noise of heavy machinery and the moving of the ladles and locos, you can imagine that the village must have been a 'lively' place to live in. He recalled the games children played, in particular setting sail on the canal just outside their back gate, in an old tin bath, with a lump of clay to seal the hangup hole. He remembered a young friend who jumped into the water to retrieve a football, forgetting he couldn't swim, and the boy's dad, who luckily was in his backyard, vaulting the wall and diving in to save him, even though the man had a club foot. It was in the nick of time for the little lad was floating face down in the water, but he lived.

Another tale was of Kevin's Father collecting discarded wood from the cooling station on the works and floating it down the canal to make a fence of it. He reached his gate, standing on the wood to float it across to the right side of the canal, when it began to sink as Kevin and his Mum watched. He just managed to jump off in time - I can imagine their hilarity. The firm allowed the workers to use such discarded material at will, as I have learnt from other workers.

The following chapter is a description of a place known to generations of Etruscan kids like Kevin, but unheard of by those of us outside the area.

Early steam generator. Grandad Jack Dunn.

A typical Etruscan family in the early 1900s, AlfWakefield's family.
Right to left, Father and Mother, Aunt Miriam, Grandad and Grandma (Howe).

An example of family involvement at Shelton Bar
The Allen — Dunn Family

Grandfather – William Henry Allen

Blastfurnaceman – had crippled hands due to pulling ropes, deaf & partially sighted in later life.

1908-60 (52yrs.)

Great Grandfather – Jack Dunn
1866-1922 (56yrs.)
Began work at 8. Became 'Cornist' engine driver.

Grandfather – Jack Dunn
1902-47, crane driver – killed at 45 when crane fell on him.

Hilda's brothers:-

Albert Allen
1926-77 (51yrs.)
Manager at 'Bottom End.'

Hilda Allen = **Stanley John Dunn**
1935-74 (38yrs) – began at 14. Sinter plant worker and fitter till death at 52. Received 25yr. service award from M.D. Mr. Field.

Bill Allen
1946-81 (35yrs.)
Labourer & rivet supporter

Frank Allen
1944-70 (26yrs)
Plater

Kevin Dunn
1960-67 (7yrs)
Template shop Fabricators ''. Later drawing office, then left to training and became lecturer

Susan
1965-78 (13yrs.)
office worker.

Stephen Dunn
1974-2000 (27yrs.)
first welder and boilermaker, then maintenance worker.

Brother-in-laws
John Pointon, train driver,
Teddy Tomkinson blacksmith (40yrs)

Grandad Jack's brother – Fred (18yrs.)

his son, **Terrance** (5yrs.)

daughter, Carol
1964-94 (30yrs)

+ Years of service through daughters of Grandads:- **brother-in-laws George** (38 yrs.), **Jack** (40yrs.)—his daughter **Beryl** (12 yrs)

GRAND TOTAL OF COMBINED FAMILY SERVICE :— 573 years!

'Cornist', with probably Great-Grandad Dunn on the footplate.

Twenty-two
MACALONIE - 'MACCA' for short

"Have you never heard of 'Macalonie'?" asked Kevin Dunn.

"No, I haven't. What is it?" I asked.

"Well, everybody born and bred in Etruria knew Macalonie! It was the heritage of all the kids born there, their own, magic playground. It consisted of all the rough ground that went from Fowlea Brook at one end of the village, towards and through Shelton Bar, along the canal and onto the Grange at Cobridge, and stretching out towards Longport. Every kid knew Macalonie almost as soon as they could speak!"

"But where on earth did that name come from?"

"Well, now you're asking something!" said Kevin. *"There have been many explanations suggested but no-one is quite sure. A few centuries back an Italian governess came to teach the Bagnall children who lived at the Grange: some think it's a corruption of 'macaroni' due to this Italian influence. Unfortunately she brought the plague over with her (in 1647), and died of it along with the Bagnall children and many more. They called her 'Singing Kate', and some fancifully suggest that, along with the burial 'hole' they put her in, that went to make up the name Macalonie."*

I discovered later, from a small book written just after the Garden Festival by Elaine Bryan and Neville Fisher, that the most likely derivation of the name came from K. Horton of Holmes Chapel, who pointed out that the name on an iron bridge over a stream towards the Grange in the area was: *Mac Elhone, Iron Founders, Glasgow.* Later I was able to verify this from another source.

Whatever, 'Macalonie' is a delightful part of Etruria foklore! Many were the games and pastimes enjoyed on this enchanted land, where explorers ventured far, often I suspect against their parents'wishes or without their knowledge. There were many dangers, especially for non-swimmers, because of the various pools, not to mention the canal; there was rubbish, dust and pollution and even toxic substances, and the obvious dangers of the nearby industries. The youngsters would find untold fascinations in this, just as I did myself as a small child visiting my grandmother in another part of our city, where shards from the potworks would serve as 'fish and chips' in our make believe shop, which we built out of thrown away bricks!

Boys swam in warm industrial pools - with convenient hollows for stripping off unseen - and grand swimming in the canal. Some boys dived off the canal bridge over the main street. They would swim past the pottery works, right through the iron and steel works, and on after that as far as they could go! At the bottom of the village Kevin and his pals would go 'jack-piking' and newt catching, or perhaps train spotting on the railway.

The Fowlea Brook channel had been altered when the railway came. Another Etruscan friend told me that the brook was always filthy and smelly, and in one part made worse by a thick, slimey, white substance which came into it from the Wedgwood potbank. The kids called this the 'Milky Way'! There must have been a natural spring nearby for there was a deliciously clean and fresh pool of water, where the newts thrived, which was used to serve a number of allotments, situated behind the row of small terraced houses which flanked the main road on the Forge Lane side. Beyond this pool was a tip of red ash.

You can imagine dens being built and wrecked on 'Macalonie', because there were gangs: the bottom enders were the gas works gang, and the great divide was the canal. They had 'clod' fights with the other end kids. There would be cowboys and indians for sure, damming of streams, treasure hunting and many another exciting game for the generations of Etruscan kids. And they would all have gone home filthy, with ripped clothes and bodies ripe for weary mums to spank and scrub and scrape!

They had sports too, football and cricket, with matches organised against teams from other areas. As the young folk reached their teens (from as young as 12 in early days, to 14 and later 15 in the 20th century) they would turn naturally to pottery, steel or mining for their jobs: and so the family traditions of work in Etruria grew through the years.

On the main Etruria canal bridge people enjoyed watching the horses which towed the barges of materials for potworks farther along the canal at Longport. At the bridge they had to change to the opposite towpath. The ropes were removed and the horse would find its own way up the side of the bridge, pass over a horse bridge and down the other side, where the ropes were reattached by the bargee, and the journey proceeded. The young lads used to collect the 'oss muck' for their family allotments. The towpaths were private and people could be fined for going down there; this was sensible from the safety point of view.

Some Shelton Bar sheds were right beside the canal, and a big gantry came out over the water, from which a crane lowered a sling of hot girders into the actual canal to cool, lifting and dipping them in again, the water sizzling and steaming, warming up the water in the Hallfield Pools nearby! Once a boy dived from the bridge and was caught up in reeds and died. Sometimes boys would gather the tow ropes of barges moored by the side - presumably while the bargees were enjoying a pint in the canalside pub - and tug them along in the water! I wonder if they were ever caught?

Twenty-three
MORE TUNNEL VISION

One great mystery remained for me about Macalonie: how come a metal bridge from Glasgow came to be erected on ground in the middle of Shelton Bar Steel Works, renowned for its bars, girders and bridge work, and its expertise in making anything required on the spot?? There is another story here somewhere and the answer came from another one time Shelton worker.

Mr. Eric Yates, now retired, lived as a boy during the 1920s in Etruria. He had good memories of 'Macalonie Bridge', which was just a footbridge he told me, situated at the far end of the Festival site and the Grange, near to the firm called 'Air Products'. He never noticed a name on the bridge, but he explained that it was made of tubular steel, which Shelton did not produce. So here is the probable answer - not so much a case of 'coals from Newcastle' as 'tubular steel from Glasgow'!

Eric had good reason to remember the bridge, since, in later years, as an employee of a demolition firm, he helped to take it down! He remembers swimming in warm pools in the area, where a great amount of rubbish was dumped by Shelton Bar. He never thought it dangerous to play there - kids don't see danger as we know, especially when they are having a good game.

At 14 Eric went to a job as a tally-boy in the time office, under boss Tommy Mitchell. He went in short trousers (just like Les Hall) because his parents couldn't afford to buy him long ones! Though he only worked there for eighteen months he knew many of the workers names, because of the time sheets. On pay day Eric handed the man's disc out of a window, then the man moved to the next window, to receive his pay. When you reached the age of sixteen, having worked for Shelton Bar, you could take your pick of jobs available at the time.

Eric recalled Forge Lane, where there was a large house on the left going in towards the works, probably lived in by one of the bosses. There was a big white wall, and that was where the men used to fight, usually having fortified themselves well beforehand at the 'Lamb Inn' on the corner. On the other corner was 'Snip Jack Owen's', the barber's shop. The other barber in Etruria was called the 'Demon Barber' - perhaps with such a name he took a great deal off!

On the left hand side of the main road, as you looked towards the bottom (railway station) end of the village and past the site of Etruria Church, was Belmont Road. This had a Co-op on one corner, and a dilapidated empty house on the other. In about 1933, Eric and his playmates went down the cellar of this house, and followed a tunnel which led off under the main road. It was full of debris and very dark and the children only had one candle, so they didn't go far, possibly 15 or 20 feet. Eric recalled finding a 1797 penny in the cellar there. The general belief of the children was that 'Josh' (Josiah Wedgwood) came from Etruria Hall to the big house by tunnel to discuss business. In those days it was not too safe to venture far alone because there were muggers even then - perhaps more desperate than today's! When this house was demolished a sub-station was built in its place, and Eric felt that the builders could easily have passed near where the tunnel was. Other workers, who spent longer at Shelton Bar, felt that he could have remembered the siting of the big house wrongly, that it could have been further away.

Savage blow when steel plant closed . . . then a new beginning

Victory out of defeat

THEY fought like tigers throughout the 1970s to save their jobs at Shelton Bar, and in their hour of victory came defeat.

The steelmen of North Staffordshire had been promised the investment they needed to preserve their employment, yet, in almost the same breath, they were told a change of heart meant they were out of work.

Almost overnight in early 1979, 180 acres of Shelton Bar became the single largest derelict site in the West Midlands.

Seven years and millions of pounds and manhours later, the gaunt rusting blast furnaces have given way to a festival the like of which has never been seen in Britain before.

Trent but almost everything achieved on the Etruria site is on a grander scale than ever before.

Reclamation has been undertaken on acres which have suffered from the ravages of the worst forms of industrial pollution since

Thumping noises . . . unusual smells . . . a red glow at night . . . fond memories of 'The Bar'

● Steelworker Jeff Cartlidge pauses to reflect on the last day of Shelton Bar. Photo: HORACE WETTON

Buzzer signals last rites for men of steel

By Sentinel reporter
Sarah Chapman

From the Sentinel

Twenty-four
THE VIC THEATRE'S *FIGHT FOR SHELTON BAR*

The 1970s' fight to save the steel making section at Shelton Bar was a long struggle. The men set up their own Action Committee, and the New Vic Theatre produced a moving documentary on their plight called *The Fight for Shelton Bar*. The Theatre had already earned a fine reputation for supporting local causes and the quality of their productions in the round was an inspiration to theatre lovers from a wide area.

The show was a musical documentary, highlighting the workers' fight against bureaucracy, and proved to be entertaining, realistic and very lively. It wove together twin themes of the fight the workers were making to keep the works going and the five basic processes of steel making in simplified terms. (The preparation of the ore for the sinter plant; the making of pig iron in the blast furnace; the converting of iron and scrap into molten steel in the Kaldo vessels; the casting of the steel into blooms in the concast machines; and making the final product - steel sections for building and industry - in the rolling mill).

The show was a great success and marvellous publicity for the steelmen. Here is an example of the many songs that formed part of the documentary:

One hundred and fifty years have passed
Since Shelton Bar was built;
How can we let our history go
And not feel any guilt?

Our fathers and our families
Have lived and worked and died.
Their monument is Shelton Bar,
Their legacy is pride.

from Part I of *The Fight for Shelton Bar*

The Director of the show, Mr Peter Cheeseman, made some interesting notes on his visits to the steel works, which are well worth quoting:

'*The Fight was to preserve a precious human institution that was harmonious and industrially efficient. This is the kind of works where there are often three generations of the same family working together: a network of uncles, brothers, grandfathers, sons, sisters and brothers-in-law stretching across its 3,000 workers.*

The human continuity and the history and heritage of Shelton Bar is symbolised in its fires. Since the first blast furnace was blown in 1841 the fire has never gone out! Right through the depressions, wars, general strike, even Nazi bombings (when great tin sheets were used to hide the glow from the tapping of the furnace or the tipping of the slag) work has gone on..... Earth and fire! Clay and coal! That's the Potteries! The blast furnaces could not go out or a cold, fifty feet thick lump of solid slag and iron, weighing hundreds of tons, would have to be disposed of and an entire furnace re-built!

Conveyor belts rattle, rumble and squeak; motors whine; screens rattle; mixing drums clatter; tannoys bleep and call out recorded warnings about sections starting and stopping..... all very confusing to a layman.'

The sinter plant is '*a long, moving firegrate, where iron ore, coke and limestone fuse together, and then drop off the end with a crash, in big slabs to be cooled and broken up for feeding into the furnaces. Protective helmets had to be worn and were colour coded: silver on the blast furnaces, red on the steel plant, green in the rolling mill, and white for executive staff, managers and visitors - the men said there seemed to be more and more of the latter!*

The blast furnace routine is a mighty, perpetually recurring drama, culminating in an elemental outburst of spectacular light and heat, as the molten metal runs like a luminous soup down its channel of sand to the waiting wagons. Sparks fizz and jump out as it hits a point of moisture, and various impurities oxidise like fireworks. The men shield their faces from the searing heat, standing in odd postures or skipping over the runners to divert the flow into a second or third wagon..... At times the hot air blasts away, bells ring, hooters blast, commands are called out..... In the build-up to the climax there is a routine of movement and preparation, a gradual increase in the tempo and anxiety in the men's movements, as they work away between the casts - clothes ruined..... There are hisses of steam here and there, extra to the constant roar.

The case for its continuance had always been *'strongly local and social'*. Now with major changes in the steel world the only way to make British steel competitive internationally was to close small works like Shelton Bar. The people of the area could not see that at all. Sympathy for Shelton Bar was intense.

Peter Cheeseman described the scene of all the pipes around and above the old furnaces, rebuilt dozens of times since 1841, layered, adapted, codged, extended, like old farm buildings: *......and you could see the sky as you looked up throught the tangle of metal and noise as dense as smoke!* He marvelled at the spectacular dimension the night gave to the many fiery displays in the plant. He was surprised to find *"pride, real dignity, sometimes even exultation. Round the edge would be the drifters watching, but the core of steelworkers showed 'total, historic dedication'!"* He was amazed by the physical relationship of men and heat, the movements of the body that were particular to shield the body from the heat.

'A semi-circular tour around a fifteen foot perimeter of revolving vessel, tilted down so that the foreman could inspect the brick lining for faults; the co-operative movements of two-man teams, who drag heavy screens to sample the molten steel with a long spoon; the swift lunging of another team shovelling the final additives into the Kaldo's white-hot mouth, and then circling back to the heap to avoid the next men's forward run!'

'Mill rollers were the master craftsmen, the mill a cavernous shed, pierced by long shafts of light from the high windows....the great bulk of the three cooler stands, with control towers perched on top of gantries straddling the steel, as it goes back and forth, then clatters off to the next section....'

Peter Cheeseman said, *"For me the whole point of the battle is that people and their natural and living communities must always come first. Any strategy or ideology which must ride over, kicking them out of the way, must be challenged, fought and defeated. Above all Shelton Bar IS its people, a deep-rooted, living and richly successful human community. That is one of the reasons it makes a profit."*

The poetry and vitality of Mr Cheeseman's descriptions gives the reader a sense of excitement, almost a feeling of being there.

The Local Newspaper entitled its final report on the end of steelmaking at Shelton Bar: WON THE ARGUMENT - BUT LOST THE BATTLE.

In the 1972-3 period Shelton Bar was making half the entire annual profit for BSC. They were sometimes referred to as the 'clog iron brigade', making steel columns for factories and bridges - the 'bread and butter' division of steel making. The rest of the steel industry was costing the tax payer £10 million a month! The next year, despite being on a three-day week, Shelton matched this performance, and in the following year they made a monthly profit of £650,000. Yet the threat of closure loomed over them.

Mr Bob Cant, Labour MP for Stoke Central, led a seven-man delegation to Westminster to seek assurances on Shelton's future, and said that what he thought about BSC's shoddy treatment of Shelton's men of steel was unprintable! The Vic-Theatre did their musical documentary and the Action Committee made many trips to London to put their case to BSC. But it was all to no avail, for finally Shelton steel production was brought to an end, because they were too small to fit in with the rationalisation plan of the BSC (June 23 1978).

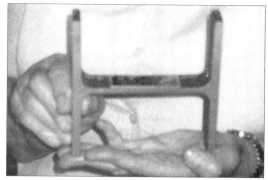

One of 150 sections made by Dave Seddon from the last bar rolled at Shelton.

To commemorate the eight year struggle for survival at Shelton Bar, Mr Colin Melbourne, sculptor and artist, then working at the North Staffordshire Polytechnic, was commissioned to create a life size statue of a steelman. This is now situated beside the impressive City Museum in Hanley, on the Broad Street side, the main road from Stoke into Hanley. It is a lasting tribute to a great industry.

The model for the statue, which was done in clay and metal, was Mr Jesse Clarke, aged 56 at the time, who worked as a blastfurnaceman at Shelton for 32 years. Modestly he said he was chosen just because he happened to be there. He had spent countless hours face-to-face with the white hot heat of the furnaces. Later he worked at the effluent plant on account of ill health. He was ribbed by his mates about being a model - one can imagine it! He did five sessions. Seven members of his family worked at Shelton Bar over 70 years; his father was a smelter all his life; his uncle started at 14 and retired at 65; his brother spent most of his working life there; and 2 brothers-in-law and a cousin also worked for the firm. Jesse said: *'The surroundings were certainly not pretty, and in the old days we worked 56 hours a week, and sometimes went all day without a meal. But funnily enough I loved every minute of it. There's something about the job that gets you. And the men at Shelton are great. I have been in the army, but I have never come across such a set of lads!"*

The steel sculpture was cast by Goodwin's Engineering, Hanley, of a special formula that should last at least 400 years. In 1973 it was paraded through London on a lorry by the Action Committee.

Twenty-five
SHELTON STEELWORKS OPEN DOOR - MAY 1994

For the second year running 'Shelton Bar' opened their doors to the public, and my husband and I joined a small group one sunny evening to be shown round the works. After a preliminary talk we were kitted out with overalls, tin helmets, goggles and ear muffles, and escorted into the mill by a friendly and informative workman guide.

We were struck immediately by the immense size of the mill - it looked a mile long - with its tremendously high roof, where dust and metal shavings could be seen rising in the wide shafts of sunlight from the high windows. High up on each side of the mill there were walkways, for easy access for maintenance work when needed, for lighting, cameras and electrical mechanisms associated with the ventilation, which is operated by push button from the ground.

About 420 people are presently employed in the mill, 70 per shift, and a 7-day week worked round the clock. Shelton has to work flat out to make a profit, for if the works come to a standstill they lose out to the tune of £110 per minute! The most lucrative work they were doing at the moment was for the emerging democracy of South Africa, and they had had to jump in quick to capture the market. They need to be constantly on their toes to grab any new work, to be viable in today's competitive world steel industry. The expression 'rolling into a country' is used when a new market in another country is captured. Steel blooms (cold steel bars) are brought in by rail from Teeside and Scunthorpe (these latter being of inferior quality) and stored in a large warehouse next to the section rolling mill. Most of Shelton's production is constructional steel work, rolled steel joists (universal beams), channels and large section angles - though not much of the latter nowadays - and 'dog's bone' sections. When split the latter become guide rails for lifts. In the 1970s Shelton was the only works in the country making these, and was ahead of the Japanese in this process. Spoilt steel is called 'cob steel', and this has to be returned to Teeside for re-working. Nothing is lost. Some firms want blue steel, ie unexposed to the elements, and this creates difficulties for storage. Some customers are fussy, and may even decide they no longer want the order after it has been made; then Shelton are left with it on their hands. Some firms try to knock down the price originally agreed upon. All this kind of thing has to be coped with by Shelton because 'the customer is always right'.

The whole mill is controlled by computers, and these are housed in high control rooms on gantries straddled across the mill and called surprisingly 'pulpits', from which the operators look down through large front and side windows to see that their particular process in the rolling mill is going ahead successfully. Some have television screens as well to check on the processes.

As we are taken along a walkway towards the first pulpit, immediately on our left is the closed-off power house for the whole mill, and on the right the great furnace of white hot metal. The heat and the dirt and the noise are daunting, but exciting and awesome. We mount the steps to the first pulpit, which overlooks the whole length of the mill, where one man is in charge of long rows of computer and television screens, gears, levers, switches and buttons on

The DEMAG Mill, 1990s.

great control panels. He has worked at Shelton Bar for over 20 years, and is one of the few who have been employed here since before the big close down of iron and steel making in 1978. He is calm and quiet, answering questions if we speak loudly enough, for there are constant crescendoes of noise. From here all aspects of the primary section of the mill are controlled - materials, sizes, quantities, temperature, timing and other factors. The controller has large viewing windows as well as television screens to be certain that all goes well.

We are looking down now to the furnace of white hot metal, as half its horizontal side opens at the base, like a mighty mesh door, and spews out horizontally a white hot length of squared steel. This is rolled across to its channel down the mill, where it is clamped by the two great metal jaws of the manipulator, and moves through what looks like a huge 'mangle' to us ordinary citizens, called 'the breakdown rolls' (the DEMAG machine imported from

Germany). It has high pressure jets of water spurting all over it, the force must be tremendous, and as the length of metal passes through for its initial shaping, steam hisses, splinters of red hot metal spit out in all directions, and black and brown bits of surplus metal 'jig' off the beam. It is a mighty inferno scene! The beam returns, the jaws unclamp, and the beam is whipped over automatically (the noise is hard to imagine), clamped again and re-rollered through the breakdown rolls. All this happens 4 times, the first 3 for elongation and the 4th for pre-forming the shape. Meantime, back at the furnace, the other half of the massive, low, mesh door opens, and the white hot twin of the first beam is pushed out, and begins its noisy journey down a twin channel.

We are back on the walkway now, and facing into the furnace, but not for long! We see the white hot depth fleetingly as we hurry to escape from the intensity of heat, dirt and noise! Our guide tells us that sometimes things can go wrong at the breakdown rolls and the metal rears up over the machine (no-one knows why, it just happens occasionally, he said), and then everything has to stop. It is hard work removing this 'cob' steel and such a stoppage causes great financial loss to the firm. It is even worse if the bar goes underneath the roll stand, into the flume of water being supplied from both ends underneath.

We pass on through the mill, to the roughing and the finishing rolls. We are led up to further pulpits, where the operator sits before a large panel of levers and switches, on a big swivel chair like a throne, and he is using his hands and his feet as well to deal with all the various parts of the system. He sits before a huge viewing window to the scene below, and has television screens as well to the side and in front of him above the window; different dials to check quality, temperature and other essential things. It is quite mind blowing to us visitors. There are computers too to keep note of orders, quantity and every other aspect of the material being worked on. In one pulpit a worker is making hand written notes for the next shift because one of the computers has broken down. The men are good humoured, willing to answer questions, joking and pointing to the most important piece of equipment - the kettle for the tea making!

Somewhere on our progression down the mill our guide points out with pride a massive machine, which is unique in the world to Shelton. This is a gigantic crane (*see end of chapter) called a 'goliath crane' for lifting the heaviest machinery. He points out huge hooks suspended on massive ropes for lifting extremely heavy loads. 180 tons can be lifted with safety, though they are actually capable of lifting nearly twice that weight!

The operator in the final pulpit, who oversees the finished beams going off to the final stacking section, says his job is the most boring of all the control jobs, because, other than in emergency, his work is just to watch for eight hours, as the beams roll through: he is ready to go immediately into manual override should anything go wrong, so he has to be constantly attentive! Poor man, he must have much patience and dedication.

When we pass on to the last section of the mill, our guide makes sure that we are wearing all our safety gear, especially the ear muffs, because he says this is the most dangerous part of all! Safety precautions are always in order, but a man can get careless and lose half a limb in a brief moment. The longest beams are being moved across the mill for stacking, and orders are made up ready to load onto wagons for delivery to customers. This last cooling and finishing section has rollers across the mill, with up-jutting metal stoppers at regular intervals (like a shark infested sea!). Great cranes controlled from high gantries lift the beams and stack

Mrs Field helping with the last firing in 1978.

them into position; unbearably, incredibly noisily.

The fuel used in the mill is gas, with oil as a backup in case of need. The firm closes for just a couple of weeks a year, for maintenance work to be done.

The set-up of the entire mill is impressive, with so few men controlling the vast enterprise. Throughout the visit we have been in admiration of the men's dedication, their ready humour and their willingness to answer any questions. The whole atmosphere of the works gives ample proof of the firm's longstanding reputation for excellent products and worker relationships.

We walk out of the dust and clamour of heavy industry, and wind our way back in the still shining evening sun to the starting place of our visit, a large reception room, where welcome coffee and biscuits await us in all our grime and exuberance.

Notes:

1) Les Hall explained his own theory about 'cobbles':

The cause of 'cobbles' - the rearing up of the steel at the breakdown rolls - is the rolling speed. When I started at the Bar, the 32" mill ganger (foreman) taught me how to take a short cut across the rolling mill by stepping over the hot bars being rolled. He said: *"The first thing to look for is the head of the bar coming towards you, and stand well clear as it has a tendency to buck. When the head has passed make sure the bar is running fast and smooth, step forward with confidence and step over."*

All very simple and I became quite an expert. I enquired what happened when the bar bucked? *"Nothing much,"* he replied, *"The pulpit operator sees the buck and immediately reduces the rolling speed, and when he sees the bar head sink to ground level, he increases the speed again."*

In the 32" mill, which was manually operated, this was not a problem, and there were no cobbles. The present Universal Mill is an automatic mill (with manual override) and it runs at twice the speed of the old 32" mill, and the pulpit operator has no chance to prevent a cobble resulting from a buck.

In the early 1970s we had the miners' strike and the M.E.B. reduced the electricity supply by 35%. This meant that I had to call for slow rolling of the mill to reduce the electricity consumption. During this period no cobbles took place, which gave weight to my theory.

I took this up with the Mill Manager, and his reply was, *"Whilst I have no argument with your theory, I cannot slow roll to save a few cobbles. Production requires that we run flat out. Anyway, what's a few cobbles? Keeps the workforce on their toes, making sure they don't get clobbered. When it happens they clear it away with all speed, as they realise for every minute the mill stands idle their bonus reduces!'*

Les adds, the words 'cob' and 'cobbles' never existed before 1964!

2) Why is Shelton unique with its lifting crane?

a) Because it is a Goliath crane being used inside a building, the only steelworks in the world using one so. All overhead cranes inside buildings are mounted on end carriages which run on rails mounted on top of the main building columns. Goliath cranes are always used outside when a building or cover is not required, ie on stocking grounds for coal, coke, ore, steel, and extensively on docks. A goliath crane is mounted on legs which have base wheels running at ground level on rails.

b) Shelton is the only steel mill in the world to be built on land with coal mines underneath.

c) When the design of the building was taking place it was soon realised that to mount a normal overhead crane on the building columns, to support the weight of the crane plus the 180 tons lifting capacity required to lift the breakdown rolls, would need foundations of a terrific size and spread, to compensate for any possible mining subsidence. Also if subsidence should occur, with a gantry type crane, levelling and jacking up the rail at a high level would be extremely difficult. The goliath crane was the answer to the difficult problem and serves the purpose well - but it has its problems:

In other mills where gantry type cranes are installed it is customary to have two cranes, a heavy duty one for lifting roll stands (250 ton capacity), and a light duty one (7 ton capacity) for general maintenance work. Shelton has no such facility and has to use the 250 ton capacity Goliath crane for both duties. This is extremely uneconomical, as the Goliath crane is so huge and slow, moving down the mill at a crawl, that it is not ideal for carrying light maintenance loads of up to 5 tons. Shelton, quickly aware of the problem, requested a quotation for an additional crane, but with all the start up costs it couldn't be afforded.

At about this time Shelton heard that at the large power station being built on the west coast of Anglesey 2 Goliath cranes (150 ton and 25 ton capacity), being used for the erection would be sold at scrap price after completion of the power station. The crane engineer and Les went over to inspect, to see if the 25 ton unit would be suitable for Shelton. The electrical equipment was good and suitable, the working height was ideal, but the flange wheels would not fit Shelton's running rails; also the width was short, and thus the span frame would need re-design and build. All the various costs made it unviable for Shelton and the matter was dropped. No additional crane was ever purchased and to this day Shelton gets by with only a mammoth goliath!

Twenty-six
FITTING FINALE

The last couple of weeks of June, 1999, have been sad ones indeed for the city of Stoke-on-Trent and for the Etruria Steelworks in particular, for the 'man of steel' himself has gone to his rest. The funeral of Mr Ted Smith, champion of the works, city and its people, took place on Friday, 25th. On the same day came the official announcement that 105 jobs have to go at 'Shelton Bar' - shattering news that might herald the complete shutdown of the works. It is uncanny that these events should happen together. A few days previously I had overheard two elderly men chatting in a big store:

One said, *"'ast 'eard about Teddy Smith dyin'?"*

The other replied, *"Ah, I 'ave. It's a sad thing and a great loss to the city.'*

They went on to compare notes about Ted and their time on the Bar, speaking with respect and admiration for him. It was the first time I'd heard him called Teddy.

Ted Smith was born and bred in the Potteries, whose past and future he cared about passionately. He left school at 13 and joined his father down the pit. Then, after 3 years in the R.A.F., he went to work in the Time Office at Shelton Bar, where he eventually became shop steward for the Wages and Timekeepers. Then he was made Vice-President of the Iron and Steel Confederation. He led the fight in the 1970s to save the works from complete shut-down, working with energetic diplomacy, and earning the respect of colleagues, citizens and officialdom. Altogther Ted worked at Shelton for 25 years, and then he moved into local politics, serving as Deputy Council Leader and then as Leader later on for 7 years. He worked indefatigably to find new jobs for redundant workers.

In the 1980s he was at the forefront of the campaign to stage the second of Britain's garden festivals at Etruria, when Shelton Bar's monstrous scenes of dereliction would be transformed into an area of beauty once again. As he predicted this was to be the provider of thousands of new jobs in the city. He was honoured at the stone laying ceremony for Festival Park after the garden festival, at which he said: *"I am delighted with this development. This area has come alive again. When you talk about employment you talk about happiness."*

The Regional Director for the development company said of him: *"Ted Smith's name is synonymous with this site. He battled to save the steel works and campaigned to replace jobs. We are delighted to be able to pay tribute to his fighting spirit."*

'Battling' and *'fighting spirit'* are indeed the right words to use in regard to Mr Smith! Few people in general knew that he had begun a fight for personal survival as early as 1987, for he never let ill health interfere with his work. He underwent a gruelling 16 hour operation in 1988 to have a diseased hip and pelvis replaced (by stainless steel!). Unfortunately his body rejected the metal, and in April 1989, his leg had to be amputated. Apparently, even on the operation day, his sense of humour did not desert him, for he is reported to have quipped, *"I knew my body would reject the steel - it wasn't made at Shelton Bar!"*

Within a few months Ted was back doing his lively work for the city he loved, *'supercharged'* to use his own expression. I also cannot help but note that this is a case of history repeating itself; that other great man, Josiah Wedgwood, who brought Etruria into being in the 18th Century, also had only one leg!

Roy Brassington, who was killed in a road accident in 1977,
the week before he was to retire. He was foreman bricklayer
in charge of three furnaces for 30 years.

Bob Lamond and Stan Whalley on the derelict site of Shelton Bar steelworks.

Now, Ted Smith, this larger-than-life member of the city of Stoke-on-Trent has gone and many tributes have flowed in. The one I like best came from a letter to 'The Sentinel' from a workmate on the Bar: *"one of the nicest and most intelligent people you could wish to know.....* *He battled with the empty headed bureaucrats, the red-tape thinkers who ran the Country, and he lost. But he still came out on top, fighting for the city as we see it today."*

A fitting epitaph you will agree.

TRIBUTES TO STEELMAN WHO FORGED CITY'S NEW SKYLINE

● Above: 1977 - Ted working with Peter Cheeseman of the New Vic on the Fight for Shelton Bar docu-drama.

● Right: 1978 - Ted as chairman of the Shelton Bar Action Committee .

● Second right: 1985 – Ted plants a tree on the National Garden Festival site.

On April 28th 2000 came the sad and complete end for the famous Shelton Works, taken over by Dutch firm, Hoogovens in 1999 (later becoming CORUS), after a general decline in the steel industry following privatisation of British Steel in 1989. The sadness of the workers is intense, a way of life has faded out of existence. At a memorial service for Shelton Bar, held at Shelton Church on Sunday, on 7th May, the Bishop of Stafford stressed that all must face the future with hope, that new types of industry will rise again from the ashes of the famous fires kept burning for so long on this historic site. Stan Whalley, who worked at Shelton Bar for 31 years as a foundry man, and as a union rep for nine years, was one of the men who helped to organise the service.

People will, and must, grieve; there were obviously a number of elderly widows of ex-steelmen at the gathering, and I heard one say to some others, *"It's a lonely life, isn't it?"*

It seemed to echo the sadness of all the valiant workers that have ever worked here in Etruria, at the heart of our city.

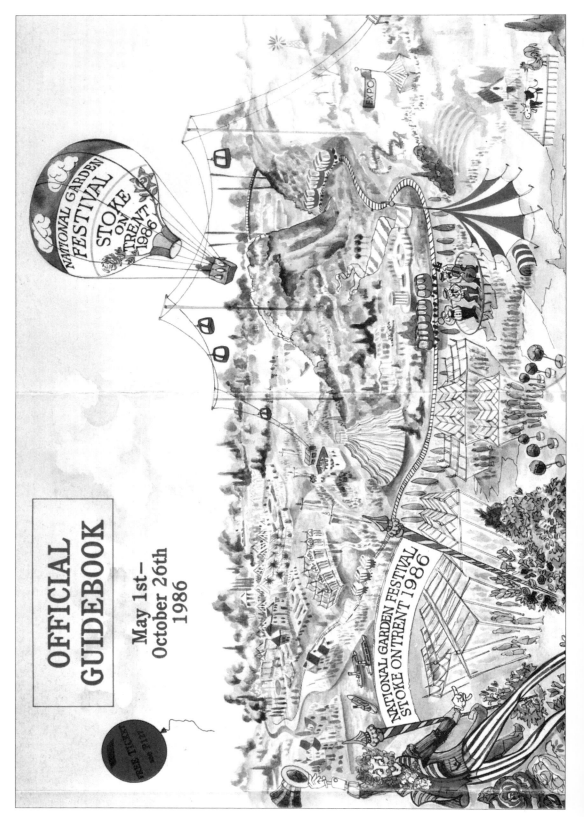

PART III

Jillivers
THE 1986 GARDEN FESTIVAL
AND FESTIVAL PARK

Top: The design masterplan model.
Centre left: A passenger carrying narrow boat similar to those found in the Festival
Centre right: The Festival light railway with rolling stock specifically built by Severn-Lamb Ltd.
Bottom: The spectacular cable car system which dominates the Festival site.

At the top the design for the three floral lakes and the floral hall, and below the cable cars.

ONE
RECLAMATION

When the British Steel Corporation closed down the steel making section of Shelton Bar in 1978, this *'largest single derelict site in the West Midlands, a focus for urban regeneration in a city with a skilled and reliable work force'* was acquired completely by the City Council. It was ideal for England's second garden festival, central to Britain's lines of communication, and within an hour and a half's journey for 19 million people! Also the site bordered the Trent and Mersey Canal with its fine potential for tourism and leisure. The go-ahead had been given for the festival as early as 1981, when the Liverpool Festival had been agreed upon, by Michael Heseltine, the Minister of the Environment. The aims for the venture were wide:

1) Complete restructuring of the site, giving opportunity for new industrial and commercial development
2) Creating a unique modern working environment, with a pleasing and lasting landscape
3) Promoting the city and the site as a prime location for new investment
4) Creating new jobs in local tourism, construction and service industries

Stoke-on-Trent, already renowned for its reclamation work, had five major headaches with this gigantic scheme at Etruria: underground dereliction from coal mining, toxic and unstable materials on the site, massive foundations of buildings demolished over a century of industrial change, a fault zone which dissected the site, and finally a lack of infrastructure.

The total cost of acquiring and reclaiming the site was estimated at £9 million, but the City and County Councils were given 100% backing by a Government Derelict Land Grant.

The earth work involved moving 1,400,000 cubic metres of material; 22,000 cubic metres of reinforced concrete, bringing in 47,000 cubic metres of sub-soil and 29,000 cubic metres of peat! Large areas had to be compacted to a depth of 4 metres, to be made suitable to support light structures. Three lakes and 2.3 miles of road with sewers and other necessary services were constructed; 35 pit shafts were capped, 148 manhole covers and 235 gullies were constructed. Masses of electric cables were removed, 33,000 volt electricity cables were layed and an 8 inch gas main made. The provision of electricity, gas, water and telecom main services cost £1,730,000!

All works were completed ahead of schedule, in spite of problems, like tar lagoons and slurry pools, excavated and stabilised for open space areas; and a buried slurry lagoon stabilised by means of jet grouting on the spot, because of the twin 33,000 volt electricity cables running through it, which served the then Wolstanton Colliery.

The National Garden Festival Company Ltd was based at Etruria Hall, and the festival was the major event in Britain and Europe for 1986. It was combined with 'Industry Expo 1986', and 20 national events were staged. The culmination was a month long celebration called 'Thanks to Industry', and a wide range of entertainments indoor and out were run for the whole six months of the festival.

Over 2,000 jobs were created. A local firm, Byrob Hire Group, supplied 32 portable buildings for the site, conveyed on 30 artics, and used for changing rooms, training units, first aid posts, police rooms, and rest areas for operational staff. Two were kitted out like theatrical dressing rooms. All were placed strategically to blend in with the festival surroundings.

The Liverpool and Stoke festivals began the run of such events, the others being in

Glasgow in 1988, Gateshead in 1990 and Ebbw Vale South Wales in 1992. In Stoke it was considered crucial to have 4 million visitors to break even, but sadly we had barely half that number, partly owing to the atrocious weather that two years. Thousands of plants had had to be discarded after the harsh winter of 1985, in fact more than £26,000 worth! Tremendously hard work was done in just the week before the opening on May 1st 1986, planting out new shrubs and plants. There were stunning displays of bulbs, many thousands planted by local school children. The weather continued poor, though we did have some beautiful days; some people, especially local old age pensioners, visited the site every day of the six months!

The restoration process begins. Top: the rose garden and a cable car station with the old Shelton ruin behind. The bottom photo shows the future Marina.

TWO
SINGING IN THE RAIN

My first visit to the Garden Festival site was in the middle of 1985's soaking wet summer, when I felt like 'Singing in the Rain' because of all the marvellous changes that were taking place on that grossly industrialised scene. The result of all the work and planning would be a fitting tribute to all the men and women who had worked so hard there in years gone by. It was midday at the secondary entrance to the Garden Festival site and the rain was absolutely teeming down. Two gatemen in waterproofs were cheerfully lifting and lowering the barrier as a steady stream of lorries, cars and trucks passed each way. A van of workmen arrived at the exit and the driver called out, *"Search this lot 'arry! they've got rose bushes and all sorts stuffed up their jumpers!"*

One of the men got out and spread his hands out on the bonnet - ready to be searched - in the thrashing rain! It was typical of the happy atmosphere in which some men had got jobs when so many had lost out, and a wonderful regeneration was taking place. The rain could not dampen their spirits.

I was waiting for a lift up to 'The Hall', in the cosy hut of the gateman, who told me he had been employed at the 18" mill in the Shelton Bar days; he was enjoying more fresh air than he had ever known while working in the mill. He was a lucky man, being one of only a handful of the old steelworkers now employed on the site. He informed me that there were 16 different contractors then at work there. No great workforce could be seen, just an odd excavator on a distant rise of ground, no-one on the streaming slopes nearby, where thousands of young plants and shrubs were being well watered in by the heavy rain. Maybe the ridiculously wretched summer had been specially ordered to consolidate the massive landscaping, and make next year's one to remember.

The 'taxi' arrived, and was driven expertly round the far from finished road up to the back of the historic Etruria Hall. The Hall was looking fairly knocked about, half of it showing its original warm red brick, and the other still covered with its unbelievable black coating of industrial grime. The famous building, restored to its former 18th century splendour, would be the centre of everything to do with the festival, surrounded by theme gardens of a wide variety, an orangerie and many other horticultural attractions.

Inside the Hall was a scene of devastation, masses of garden festival information strewn on desks and floor amongst the dust and debris, workmen passing back and forth as they went about their various tasks, secretaries trying to get on with their jobs in seemingly total chaos. A courteous young landscape designer, Mr Francis Colella, gave me some of the brochures and then drove me slowly round the site, explaining about all the pattern of gardens, pavilions and other attractions being planned. It was impossible to imagine what the seven-tented structure resembling an Arabian Night's scene would be like, though the trellis walk over which roses and other shrubs would climb in profusion was already in place. We visited the festival rose garden, already complete, with its thousands of peach floribunda scenting the air in delicious profusion, all around the special place for the statue of that other great potter, Sir Henry Doulton. The Dutch Garden, transferred from the Liverpool Festival, was in place and had attractive pools and pavilions.

FESTIVAL PARK
Stoke-on-Trent

WOODLANDS   LAKESIDE

OFFICE OF
ST MODWEN PLC

THE GLADES

KI
E

RAL WOODED PARK LAND

FOODSTORE

ON-FOOD
TAIL PARK   PETROL
FILLING STATION

RETAIL

HOTEL

LEISURE

BUSINESS AND
COMMERCIAL

FUTURE DEVELOPMENT
OPPORTUNITIES

Streaming heights - 1985 was a very wet year.

Arabian Nights tents.

Etruria Hall at the start of restoration.

Staff working in Etruria Hall in helmets as restoration begins.

A head start for N.G.F. staff

Historic Etruria Hall — former home of Josiah Wedgwood — is taking a battering from builders in preparation for the 1986 National Garden Festival.

And staff working inside the 18th century building are taking no chances — hence secretaries, information officers and executives all wear hard-hats indoors.

The equipment has become as essential as typewriters and telephones and it will be "hats on" until almost the end of the year as contractors work inside and out restoring the building.

More than £100,000 is being spent on the work and the aim is to return Etruria Hall to its original design in the days of Wedgwood. The stately home is the headquarters of the N.G.F. company and, with nine months to festival opening, there was no time to close down the offices during rebuilding.

Twentieth century additions to the hall have been pulled down, windows are being replaced along with wiring, roof lines are being altered and the entire building sandblasted to reveal the original colour of the brickwork.

Beyond the three lakes, one of which was already seeded and showing signs of plant life, was the high-tech greenhouse 2000, covering an area big enough for two full size football pitches. Here would be a great horticultural layout of the City Parks Department, along with art displays and a mini-tropical area. Beyond the greenhouse rose up the massive girders of the old Shelton Bar continuous casting plant, nicknamed 'Big Bertha', a dark and menacing backdrop in the process of being demolished - giants of steel giving way to giants of glass!

A Woodland Ridge formed the backbone to the whole Festival site, on which would be discovery trails, stone circles, picnic sites, woodlands, tarns and hidden areas where children could delight in all kinds of games. The Ridge was dissected by a specially dug out valley featuring waterfalls and outcrops of rock, the suggestion of the design co-ordinator, Mr Joe Samworth, to facilitate the movement of visitors from one area to another without undue tiredness. The valley was spanned by an attractive made-to-last wooden bridge.

The land rose and fell, each slope planted with Italian evergreens and English shrubs. Three thousand pounds worth of plants had already been grown for the Festival by 1983! It would surely be a place of beauty and surprise. Many individual promoters were designing and providing their own displays, amongst them Glasgow District Council who would feature a bandstand; Newcastle-under-Lyme who would have an exciting fort; and North Staffs Moorland Council who would bring a touch of the Orient with their replica of a temple, like the one in Biddulph Grange grounds. This was being designed and built by 5th and 6th formers from Westwood High School, Leek, assisted by their teachers.

A scenic railway would carry visitors throughout the display areas, and a waterbus would ferry them along the canal to the Marina at the southern boundary of the site.

Turning east from the Woodland Ridge you could lose yourself in a labyrinth, view a dragon in bedding plants and visit an aviary of exotic birds, surrounded by gardens with flowers of the same colours. A festival farm would delight the little ones.

Oh, there was such a plethora of ideas, and the immensity of the undertaking seemed daunting! How could it all be finished on time? My guide said that in spite of the vagaries of the weather he thought that it would be; the planners had learnt from the Liverpool experience, and from other countries like Germany, who had been organising garden festivals for over 40 years when vast areas of cities destroyed by bombs had had to be dealt with. What a marvellous idea to turn devastation into areas of beauty and amenity for the people to enjoy, as well as providing new jobs. My guide said he could not wish for a more rewarding job!

My time was over and he had to return to his work. I left the site filled with enthusiasm for what these people were doing to rebeautify this historic site.

The cable cars with the Blackpool gardens below.

School children planting bulbs on a cold winter day in 1985.

THREE
RANDOM NOTES ON THE GARDEN FESTIVAL

From the beginning of the Etruria Festival the emphasis was that everything should be for the present and future benefit of the citizens of Stoke-on-Trent, not only in providing recreation and jobs, but also as a persistent quality working environment in a parkland setting. Much work had been done already on the Woodland Ridge by 1983, including the setting of 70,000 shrubs and trees, when the weather suddenly turned very warm. Stoke City Fire Brigade had to be called, to pump water from the canal and saturate the soil. They used the occasion as a training exercise and were successful in saving every single plant! An irrigation system was installed in time for the summer of 1984, when we had four very hot months - this of course being the year of the Liverpool Garden Festival.

The variety of activities at the Festival was tremendous, the 68 theme gardens forming a major interest, where there was something for all tastes. Essential sponsorships came from local businesses and from many authorities much further afield. Close co-operation was received from landscape artists, surveyors, growers and amateur gardeners, all of whom invested much talent and hard work in all the various features. "There was a strong feeling of loyalty to an area which had supported so many industries for so long," and this was to be a great community event.

Local schools were deeply involved, over 50 taking part in various activities at the festival site, including entertainment of one form or another throughout the six months, such as dance, song, drama and orchestral concerts, performed in the big top. This was kitted out like a theatre and seated 600 people. The first class to arrive on the site had been five-year-olds with plastic spades, who helped to plant wild bulbs - on the coldest day of the year! Three local secondary schools took part in a social service exercise, working a seven day week, pushing wheelchairs for the handicapped, and escorting partially sighted visitors around the site. Another secondary school set up a complete travel agency, with computers, offering advice and information, and bookings for the Festival and local accommodation.

Interesting play areas were set up all around the Garden Festival so that children could have somewhere to enjoy themselves, while their parents lingered to admire special exhibits or gardens of particular interest to them. One of the most popular was the thatched cottage garden, which surrounded a two thirds life size cottage beautifully furnished inside. Of course all the family went into this beautiful 'olde worlde' exhibit with great enthusiasm. The cottage was surrounded by a glorious array of lovely wild flowers, as well as all the garden favourites, foxgloves, cowslips, harebells, ox-eye daisies, cornflowers, marigolds, delphiniums and some vegetables and fruit as well. During the year following the festival when revisiting the site, I was delighted to see a young teacher with her class of junior pupils, going through the garden and cottage. When they reappeared they sat down to write about what they had seen. It seemed to illustrate the essence of what the city planners had had in mind.

Another immensely attractive feature was the Classic Water Garden, designed by Douglas Butterill. The Italianate fountains had eleven interchanges of jet patterns, which presented a delightful ear and eye catching effect.

During the six month festival there were hot air balloons, high fashion laser shows, clowns, stilt walkers, buskers, local small bands entertaining people at different parts of the site, and thrilled to be doing it; ideal homes exhibitions, garden and flower contests, and parades on a grand scale, some of which went through the City before their rendez-vous at the festival arena. There was a festival farm; a cable car from which you could have marvellous aerial views of the beautifully laid out formal gardens; and a scenic railway to take you all round the site, having stations where you could drop off to visit various attractions, or go to one of the 15 catering points.

Interesting sculptures dotted the festival area; a positive feature of the Stoke site was that some spots could not be built upon, and these lent themselves to exhibits of this nature. Some were retained after the festival had finished. *'The topography served as an orientation point'*.

Bill Morland in his book 'Portrait of the Potteries' makes the endearing comment that: *"There are no signs saying KEEP OFF THE GRASS in the Potteries - they lay turf and plant grass especially for people to walk on!"* Some of this walking led you to examples of the onsite sculpture which proved a great subject for debate amongst a good many people!

School children with their teacher after the Festival finished.

FOUR
FESTIVAL SCULPTURES

The festival sculpture co-ordinator and assistant, Vivien Lovell and Steve Field, determined that visitors should get involved with the 'art-in-progress' on the site, and be able to make comments and/or criticisms. They knew that far more people would see the festival in the six months than would visit art galleries in London, for example, and thus art would be brought to them in a direct confrontation. A worthy aim indeed! The 'captive audience' would be intrigued, amused, even impressed perhaps, and at times, probably, affronted! Apparently the public were not backward in coming forward with their opinions and readily offered advice to the working artists. I didn't go specifically in search of the sculptures, rather they just 'happened' to me as I wandered, and I found the whole programme very interesting and worthwhile.

Some of the work was very beautiful, particularly the 'Moon Pool', **situated near** to the front of Etruria Hall, which I visited every time I went to the festival site. It was sad to see this neglected and filthy at one stage, and I hoped 'they'would clean it up for when visitors came to the prestigious new Moat House Hotel. ('They'did!) Sadly, in the year 2000, the whole area of the festival water features in front of the Hall were in a state of utter neglect, though hopefully plans for renewal are in the offing.

There were over 100 works on site, some by famous sculptors, others by local artists - about 85 works in total. First rate cooperation was received from local industries, many in the shape of materials and facilities for making the exhibits. A host of different materials were used, some quite bizarre - like old car parts and toilet pans! I particularly enjoyed the 'Rustic Dancers' on top of the Woodland Ridge, though I remain convinced that they were really coal and steel workers demanding their jobs back! 'Sky Wedges' was another attractive and satisfying exhibit, again high on the ridge, being a 'fan' of very large thin sliced pieces of tree trunks against the skyline, where we often took our springer spaniel in the years following the festival, to roam excitedly on the grassy slopes from which they stretched out. Sadly, the elements took their relentless toll on these noble planks. Another sculpture, which was retained after the festival, was a very large lump of coal, slung above the ground by a contraption of wood, steel and leather (I think)..... a mighty token to the memory of all the miners who had worked through the years on this site. However some gardeners said it had had to be removed not long after the end of the festival, because of various assorted vandals hacking chunks of it away, and making it unsafe to be left there.

'The Whisper' by Andre Wallice, was a couple of very large teenagers sharing a secret on a bench. This gave me great pleasure, especially when I spotted it some years later on the way into London, somewhere near to Swiss Corner. I felt a warm surge of 'ownership' .

In 1991 we learnt that 9 of the best works of art specifically created for our Festival had been bought for the public, and would remain on site. This was part of the ongoing policy of maintaining a quality place for people to enjoy, whether at work or leisure. A particular exhibit, which meant a great deal to all local people, especially those who had worked on the site, was the slag ladle, which was filled with brilliant red and orange flowers to represent the molten slag. This was eventually taken back to what remained of the steelworks.

Another feature for which we have a great deal of affection is the gazebo, removed from the festival site to Hanley Park: sadly, along with the park itself, it now looks rather shabby. (Hopefully in the not too distant future our Town Council will be minded to spend some cash on this and other parks, where so many of our citizens find pleasure in the outdoors.)

I have mentioned only a few of the sculptures, but perhaps memories have been stirred.

The slag ladle from old Shelton Bar.

FIVE
FRIDAY THE THIRTEENTH

Friday, 13th June 1986, was sunny, even hot for a change, so we rounded off our holidays with a trip to the Garden Festival. The last of the tulips were in full flower, tiers and tiers of them, pansies were at their glorious best and the rhododendrons and azaleas were a riot of colour. The scene was one of overwhelming beauty. Every turning point presented some new delight to the eye, ingenious and artistic ideas abounded. We enjoyed the variety of sculptures in all kinds of media, amused by some, puzzled by others. However it was the small gardens which attracted us most of all: so much beauty achieved in such small spaces - God and man at work together.... breath-taking! I particularly liked a beautiful cascade of different shades of allysum and lobelia down a rocky streamway, which created a lovely impression of running water, such simple plants yet so effective. The dragon in bedding plants was impressive too, standing out so well against the green grass with his fiery colours.

Unwittingly, we had chosen an auspicious day for our visit, for as we stood at the top of the Southern Steps - an award winning hill topped with a huge maypole, whose stout, coloured (and waterproof!) ribbons cascaded down the slopes - we saw crowds of happy young people dressed in 18th century costume coming in at the main gates. Who could they be? Dutch dancers perhaps? They made their way excitedly onto the immaculate lawns in front of Etruria Hall, and we soon discovered that they were all employees from the Wedgwood Factory at Barlaston and other local potworks, coming as their forebears had done to be entertained by their employer and his wife - the first Josiah and Mrs Wedgwood. The young folk were welcomed by a couple impersonating the famous pair and a fine time was being had by all. Later they toured the Hall as we did, passing first to the left into a marvellous display of the many splendid figures which Doultons have produced through the years, of people, animals and fish of all sizes, some quite priceless. Particularly attractive was a display of crystal laid out amongst an arrangement of rocks, simulating icicles and running water. We watched an artist painting one of the famous Doulton lady figurines and explaining how they are made. There are two ways of painting the figurines, under glazing and over glazing, the former used for character figures and the latter for the crinoline ladies. Ceramic paints are mixed usually with aniseed or substitute, with a little glycerine added to make the putting on of the paint easier. After each layer of paint comes another firing, some pieces having as many as five, each lasting longer than a day! No wonder the figurines are so expensive! Training for the job takes two years at least, especially for the delicate face painting, and the artist puts his/her mark on the bottom of the ware.

Moving on we crossed the entrance hall and entered the right hand part of the lovely old building, where there were exhibitions all about Wedgwood and his family. Entering one room, I saw a model of an old lady in a chair by the window, apparently looking out at the scene of revelry on the lawns outside. I presumed she represented one of the old Wedgwood ladies, but as I moved closer I was astonished to see that she was real! Slowly she explained that she had been feeling unwell, and had been put by the window to recuperate a little. Just then her daughter arrived, explaining that her mother was the oldest surviving Etruscan, namely Mrs Burton, aged 92! She had been introduced to the Queen at the official opening.

Part of the West Midlands Garden to the left, and the Brighton Pavilion replica on the right.

'Every type of Wedgwood dinner plate - the effect was stunning'.

I felt thrilled to have met the old lady, but beat a hasty retreat to allow her to recuperate.

In the next room there was a thrower demonstrating his work, surrounded by the young '18th' century workers, who treated us to a merry scene. One of their number was invited to try his hand at the wheel, and he proceeded to create a certain shape, which had his mates roaring with laughter. Amidst the ribald banter the clay suddenly shot off the wheel, to the intense amusement of all the onlookers. One could well imagine the earthy good humour of the workers on the shop floor! It was hilarious.

Other rooms displayed interesting pictures and documents from the life of the great potter. Then we came upon another which quite took our breath away. It was a square shaped room and cunningly lighted to show to the very best effect every type of Wedgwood dinner plate with all the glorious patterns ever produced. Walls and ceiling were covered with these and even in the floor plates were displayed safely beneath strong, glass panels. The effect was stunning and we thought that it was the most beautiful room of all.

When we left the Hall we wandered along the Woodland Ridge, to discover a model Kenyan village, where we learnt that Kenya has the largest flower farms in the world, on the side of Lake Naivasha, where 130 million carnations are grown every year and 40 million other flowers! There was a camping site for scouts and guides up there and a Boys' Brigade display; a garden of rest, a bog garden and countless wooded areas to explore.

We realised that it was time for us to go, and after a quick purchase at the Festival Market, we headed for the massive car park. For the first time ever my husband couldn't find the car, for there appeared to be thousands there. We had a good laugh and eventually located it, and made our way home after what had been a glorious Friday 13th!

A new police shift coming on duty.

The 1986 Methodist Logo Garden.

The Dutch gardens and pavilions.

SIX
ALL THINGS NEW

My Garden

A garden is a lovesome thing, God wot!
Rose plot,
Fring'd pool -
The veriest school
Of peace, and yet the fool
Contends that God is not
Not God! In gardens! When the eve is cool?
'Tis very sure God walks in mine.

Edward Brown

This chapter title was used for the newspaper for the United Church presence at the festival. When visitors saw how 'all things had been made new' on the old Shelton Bar site, they could really see the relevance of the title. At the opening ceremony on Sunday, 4th. May, 1986, the Bishop of Lichfield talked of gardens in the Bible; Eden, Gethsemane and the wondrous garden at Easter, when Jesus first revealed himself to Mary. She thought at first that he was the gardener, and perhaps this is an apt idea - we sometimes use the phrase, 'everything in the garden's lovely' when things are going well for us. A prayer for the Garden Festival went like this:

> Lord Jesus, Son of the Living God, teach us to walk in Your Way more trustfully, to accept Your Truth more faithfully and to share Your Life more lovingly. We pray that by the power of the Holy Spirit, You would guide those who work for the Christian Church at the 1986 N.G.F. in unity, so that all may come as one family to the Kingdom of the Father where You live for ever and ever.   Amen.

In a small garden near to the Churches' Centre there was a beautiful floral version of the 1986 Methodist Logo, planned by Mr George Tomlinson, Northern Chairman of the National Dahlia Society, and executed by Crewe Parks. Another feature of special interest during the time of the Conference was an exhibition in the Churches' centre called 'This is Methodism'. The Rev. Tony Sutcliffe, one of the main organisers of the Church Presence at the festival, kindly wrote the following resume of the preparations made and the important witness given by the ecumenical teams who worked together in such happy unity. At the time I did not know Tony and his wife Mary, but in later years we had the pleasure of welcoming them into our small, though enthusiastic, congregation at Basford Trinity Methodist Chapel.

THE CHURCH PRESENCE AT THE GARDEN FESTIVAL
Within a few weeks of the announcement that Stoke-on-Trent was to host the 1986 National Garden Festival, the then Bishop of Stafford, John Walker, called a meeting of interested clergy and lay people of all denominations to discuss the possibility of a Church centre, and a programme of Christian events, to be a witness to the Christian faith. That meeting was held at Bethesda Church, Hanley, and was attended by representatives of the whole spectrum of

Christian Churches, both 'mainstream'and 'house' churches. It was quickly decided that an acre of the festival site should be acquired, and a building placed on it, and that major events should be held approximately monthly in the large marquee near the main area.

But what about cost? A small 'main' committee was elected, and a number of sub-committees formed, to look into finance, programmes, advertising, daily worship, book-stalls, exhibitions etc. And it was discovered that the cost would be at least £12,000, and probably nearer £20,000, and appeals were sent out to all the churches in Stoke-on-Trent. How wonderful to be able to say that we were never once in debt!

Finance was not the only problem - if you have a church centre for people to visit, then it has to be staffed! How shall we find enough people to cover the hours of 10.00 am to 8.00 pm every day, for the 180 days that the festival is going to be open? Who will staff the bookstall for all the time? Who will be available for catering, and who will organise it? These were some of the questions to be faced and we soon found that we were involved with a mass of logistics. But again we found that our prayers and appeals were answered. People made a wide variety of offers, some would come once a fortnight on a particular day of the week, some churches sent groups for a whole week every two months, some people came every other morning, afternoon or evening and all had to be 'slotted in' so that there were never too many or too few at any one time. Apparently insurmountable problems were solved and planning continued to go ahead in faith.

The opening service was held on the first Sunday afternoon of the festival, all denominations were represented and shared in the act of worship and dedication by the Bishop of Lichfield. Would everything work as planned? Of course there were teething problems; a flood after heavy rain during the first few days, last minute changes in personnel, but in spite of these the whole venture was a great success. Each day at noon there was a fifteen minute service, conducted by the people on the rota for the day, according to their particular rites. We had, for instance, nuns from the local convent sharing with a group from the Bethel Faith Centre, and Salvation Army officers sharing with a group from the Church of England Parish; a complete sinking of denominational differences to make a united witness to the visitors at the festival. And it worked!!

At the end of the festival, our visitors' book showed that 22,000 people from all over the world had come through the doors of the Church Centre; they had seen the weekly displays from organisations like Christian Aid, CAFOD, Banardoes, National Children's Homes etc; they had bought books, videos and tapes from the stalls; they had spoken to the 'staff of the day'; they had seen something of the Christian Faith in action!

And there were outside events: the visit of George Hamilton 1V and other gospel singers, local choirs, even a christian escapologist who used his skill to illustrate the freeing of people from the chains of sin!

The overwhelming inspiration came from the fact that all the churches worked together. When we first met there was an understandable hesitation and reserve, but as the committee worked and met together there grew a real sense of trust and enthusiasm. To be a member of the committee from its inception to its disbanding when the task was done (several months after the festival finished) was a tremendous privilege and a wonderful experience.

The late Mr Les Green with Adam the Gardener.

Design by William Gillespie for the labyrinth.

SEVEN
THE GLORY OF THE GARDEN - THE SAVPG THEME GARDEN

THE GLORY OF THE GARDEN

O, Adam was a gardener, and God who made him sees
That half a proper gardener's work is done upon his knees.
So when your work is finished you can wash your hands and pray
For the Glory of the Garden that it may not pass away,
For the Glory of the Garden shall never pass away.

Rudyard Kipling

This title, taken from the famous Kipling poem, was used by the Staffordshire Association of Village Produce Guilds, for their theme garden at the festival. It was very appropriate as proved by the thousands of visitors, and the accolades and awards it received. Three years' work, sustained by hundreds of dedicated and talented Staffs gardeners, ensured that it was an enterprise to remember for life! The story of how the 'Garden' came into being is worth telling because it was the greatest achievement of the Association in its 41 year history.

SAVPG began during the period of the Second World War when small neighbourhood gardeners' groups were formed in the drive for self-sufficiency. 'Dig for Victory' was the slogan of the time. In the 1980s there were 38 such gardeners' groups throughout the County, with 2,800 members. At least 800 of these became involved with work for the theme garden! It is astonishing to realise that over the six month period of the festival a rota operated whereby four members were on duty every single day, ready and eager to talk to visitors!

The first approach to the Association was made as early as 1984, and upon acceptance a 52 clause contract had to be signed! - just one of the many aspects being the safety on the site of workers, exhibitors and visitors. Ideas for the design came from many members and a committee was formed to co-ordinate the project, headed by Mr Roy Mowforth, former head of Rodbaston Agricultural College, and including Mr David Butcher, Association chairman, and his wife, Mr and Mrs Maurice Cliffe, Mr Brian Barwell and Mr and Mrs Les Green. The latter became co-ordinator for the scheme since he was 'on the spot', living close to the festival site. Over the next 3 years Mary, his wife, counted herself a 'Festival Widow', while at the same time helping her husband as much as she could in his enormous task. His work included design, sponsorship, information, programmes, liaison with other bodies, construction, signing, and publicity: and finally, at the end, removal of the exhibit!

Because of their early start on the project SAVPG obtained massive sponsorship, 61 firms supported them to the tune of £30,000, enabling a more ambitious design than originally planned! The drawing was finalised by Mr Francis Colella. The Association benefitted in that they had a choice of 4 different sites. They decided on the sloping area in front of the former Saint Augustine Little Sisters of the Poor on the Cobridge skyline, not an easy site but one that lent itself to imaginative planning and landscaping. Their design included raised areas of trees and shrubs, lawns and rose beds, a rockery, pools, massed flower areas, walkways and rest places; as well as a conservatory and greenhouse, and an impressive entrance of latticework and tiling and a larger-than-life sculpture of 'Adam the Gardener', sculpted by Brian Ibbeson, would welcome in the crowds to 'The Glory of the Garden'.

From the earliest days Mr Green was inundated with supplies from enthusiastic sponsors which at times completely blocked his drive at home and spilled out on to the road. Part of his job was to get the supplies to the festival site area, and he was full of praise for the many neighbours, friends, local firms and his own employers, Johnsons of Tunstall, for their unstinting help in this. The latter gave him all kinds of facilities, including the use of their lorries and their drivers, as well as as much personal time away from his own work.

Initial excavation on the site begun in late 1984, and the construction of the rockery was undertaken by a sponsor. Industrial waste and poor sub-soil was replaced by tons and tons of mushroom compost. ALL tools for the venture were supplied copiously by 'Bulldog', as well as every conceivable commodity required for the theme garden. The generosity of the sponsors was truly astonishing, and the teams of workers, overwhelmed by this, began their labours with enthusiasm and excitement. The work was heavy, even arduous at times over the next couple of years; but there was real enjoyment as the garden began to take shape, and often merriment, as the following incident shows. The group were in the process of constructing the pool, in which tropical fish loaned by a local pet shop were to be placed. They had laid the lining for the pool and were filling it with water, when one of their number found himself unable to stop on the slippery material, and in no time at all was chest deep in the middle of the pool! You can easily imagine the reaction of the others; they fell about laughing to such a degree that it was several minutes before anyone thought to offer a rescuing hand and haul him in to shore! Needless to say the victim was less than amused.

By October, 1985, the garden was ready for the planting to begin, and a sponsor provided and planted standard trees as a backdrop for the whole scheme! Six thousand seedlings were supplied by another sponsor and these were *'lovingly nurtured in members' gardens',* before being planted out on the site. The whole garden was substantially completed by mid-December 1985, in spite of abysmal weather! By April 1986 the garden was complete and the members were jubilant, having so many plants left over that they were able to make a lovely extra flower bed outside their fencing! The SAVPG. garden proved to be one of the most popular of the whole festival. Details of all the plants were computerised and displayed on a long noticeboard at the back of the conservatory, and visitors were able to chat with the volunteers on duty every day - about their favourite topic, gardening!

Judging the theme gardens at the Festival took place three times during the six months, and 'The Glory of the Garden' secured the silver gilt award at the first, the large gold at the second, and the large gold again at the third. They also received the Festival Chairman's award for the most imaginative project by a Staffordshire Organisation. The Director of 'Silvaperl', one of the group's most generous sponsors, spoke of *"the high standard of craftmanship achieved in design, construction and maintenance"* of the SAVPG.

These ardent amateur gardeners had lived up to the title they had chosen for their garden. All were sad when the festival had to end, but admitted that the enterprise could not have been sustained much longer, and the cost of maintaining any of the gardens on the site would have been prohibitive. However the intense labour of so many and the huge amount of money spent were certainly worthwhile, for it meant a wonderful regeneration of a precious piece of ground, to the benefit of millions of people who visit it annually. The group, now SAGG (Staffs Amateur Gardeners' Guild), can remember their own glorious contribution with the joy and satisfaction.

EIGHT
MEMORIES OF FORMER CITY LEISURE AND RECREATION HEAD

Mr Davis Knight, who retired in 1996, talked to me about the reclamation work at the Etruria site before the festival, and in particular about the development of the Grange open space at Cobridge, which of course included part of one of the massive spoil tips of Shelton Bar. A man had objected to their efforts to create an attractive green mound between some houses (his included) and the British Oxygen Works, because he said it spoiled his view.... of the spoil tip! He even went onto the 'Jimmie Young' radio show, during which David discussed with him the value of this kind of reclamation work..... 'There's nowt so funny as folk!'

David recalled some of the actual reclamation of the festival site - the basic renaissance of the despoiled land, the structured landscaping and planting achieved by their own engineers, and architects and by outside contractors, which gave a tremendous boost to local firms. The Woodland Ridge had been the biggest challenge of all: it would have been far too costly to cover with top soil, so Stoke-on-Trent had bought a whole peat bog and had it transferred to the site! Auspiciously for the city just such a valuable commodity (in conservation terms) had become available at the right moment, from the Lancashire Mosses, near Warrington, where a site was being cleared for the building of a new industrial complex. One might say an almost biblical exchange!

The industrial 'grot' (his word) on the Woodland Ridge was sealed in by a layer of clay and then the bog was spread over the whole. The marvellous benefit of this was two-fold; along with the bog came wildlife, flora and fauna, like wild flowers, grass snakes and butterflies. Secondly the medium proved excellent for starting off of the young trees planted, native shrubs, pioneer species, English alders (very fast growing), and all the trees we know and love, as well as beautiful groups of conifers set at intervals, which today provide magnificent displays for visitors. There is something calming and refreshing about the dark greens of conifers. The trees have grown so well that the main chore each year is cutting them back in order that people can move around this forest area of beauty and quiet.

David went on to remember the auspicious day of the official opening of the Garden Festival by Her Majesty the Queen, on May 8th 1986. This proved to be a memorable one for him in particular, and not entirely for the best of reasons! It started early and well enough, with a happy discovery of some partridge eggs on the Woodland Ridge by a gardener. However on into the highly organised day, and things began to go a little awry. Police security was obviously very tight, with plain clothes detectives and uniformed men and women on duty everywhere, so movement was restricted. Her Majesty was to take lunch at the Lakeside Restaurant and afterwards David was scheduled to accompany her on a tour round Greenhouse 2000. However, when the time came for him to make his way there, the police would not let him through! He showed them his identity card with photo and gave them the details of his allotted job, but to no avail. They must rush off to verify him with their superiors! When they returned they made him write down every single detail about himself and his important task, and then they rushed off again for further consultation. By now, David said, he was getting distinctly hot around the collar and could feel his job slipping away with the seconds! Eventually, however, they allowed him through, and he managed to arrive at

The Queen's visit.

The road to the lakeside restaurant where the Queen lunched.

Greenhouse 2000 just ahead of the Royal Party, who luckily were running late. (Phew!)

Once inside the greenhouse he began to feel some concern for the Queen, as she started to turn very pink in her warm blue hat and coat in the 72 degree atmosphere. However all went well. He related what a strange experience it was to see a police frogman emerge from one of the three large water tanks of the greenhouse, but it was a necessary precaution of course!! The visit went without a hitch, but very soon after the Royal Party's departure the 'heavens opened up' to such a degree that the rains burst through the greenhouse roof and created a flood! Fortunately no damage was caused, and needless to say the water was 'harvested' for use in house!

Mrs Knight had been right beside Her Majesty during the visit, but had felt it too intrusive to attempt to take any photographs. She and her husband David no doubt contented themselves with the ' official' records of their very special day, truly memorable for them both, though for entirely different reasons!

POSTSCRIPT

Two or three years after the Festival David Knight was enjoying a quiet inspection walk up on the Woodland Ridge, when he witnessed a strange sight: he saw a sheep dog appearing out of nowhere, and then he heard a strange whistle to which the dog responded eagerly. He rounded a corner of trees and then he saw another sheep dog and almost at once a shepherd, complete with crook and other gear! Amazed and interested he went to have a word with him. The man told him he had a sheep farm at Market Drayton (about 18 miles away), but once a week he came to the Woodland Ridge to exercise his dogs and train them, and they loved it. Meantime his wife and children were in Morrisons doing the weekly shopping! Afterwards they joined him up there for a picnic lunch. Needless to say David was delighted by this as he felt it was the essence of what Festival Park was all about, folk enjoying an outing in the green heart of an industrial city! A countryman and his family enjoying the amenities... marvellous!

Wild life on the Ridge had developed enormously and there were long lists available of all the birds and animals spotted there, as well as the lovely wild flowers. A man had offered an old badger in the early days, but this had had to be refused for legal reasons. There were domestic cats gone wild, and quite fierce too; many water birds on the lakes, and nearby office workers had formed a duck feeding club.

He gave some interesting details about other parts of the city in regard to nature; I was surprised when he said that we had a few SSSIs. in the city (puzzled too, until he explained that this meant 'sites of special scientific interest') at least one being of national interest! This is at Ford Green Nature Reserve, where some years as many as 2,000 migrating swallows gather to roost for several days on their winter journey to Africa. Also Stoke is the only city in the country where you could see all species of British owls in one area. At the time he said that there were 18 areas of wildlife importance in the city, and by now that number has certainly increased, since Stoke has continued its policy of encouraging a greener environment for all. In Stoke-on-Trent, he said, there were now more trees per head of population, ie four, than since the beginning of the Industrial Revolution - which certainly happened with a vengeance in Etruria! Finally, whereas in 1970 there were less than 2 acres of public open space per 1,000 of the population, there were now 12! This increase is unprecedented in the whole of Europe.

Through the Woodland Ridge to the Lakes.

Over the bridge and down the rocky hill road.

A meadow on the Woodland Ridge.

Percy Thrower and other celebrity gardeners came to talk in the Pavilion of Exotic Plants, and to offer advice to gardeners.

The Welsh presence at the Garden Festival

NINE

GREENHOUSE 2000

Greenhouse 2000 merits a chapter on its own, for it is a high-tech venture which will play an important role in the life of the City well into the 21st Century. It was one of the largest buildings at the festival site covering 3½ acres. Everything remotely connected with the garden was exhibited here, except for the garden itself. All the horticultural works of the City Parks and Gardens Department are housed here, presenting a revolutionary scale of gardening. Computers can turn any part of the greenhouse into a totally different environment, from tropical to arctic, and a series of weather stations throughout the building monitor outside conditions and relay information to a central computer, which controls interior temperature, watering, feeding, ventilation and sun screening.

Greenhouse 2000 was one of the Country's most advanced structures of its kind - another was built at Stockport about the same time, and there are smaller versions at Bradford and Derby. Visitors to greenhouse 2000 were shown all stages of growth, from seed sowing and cutting taking, to full grown plants. G.2000 requires 4½ million BTUs, provided by 4 gas boilers, and is double glazed with twin-skinned poly-carbonate plastic sheet material - much lighter and less maintenance than glass. A minimum temperature of 70 degrees can be maintained even in the severest weather conditions.

The tour of G.2000 at the Festival ended with a visit to a tropical garden with water features, where exotic butterflies and moths could be admired flying at liberty. These were the property and lifelong passion of Bill Wheatley of Endon, director of North Midlands

Greenhouse 2000 with Shelton Steel Sheds behind.

Butterflies, and experts were on hand to talk to. Incidentally the winner of the best photo competition at the festival was a friend of mine who snapped her small grandson gazing in amazement at one of the exotic butterflies.

It was predicted that with the closure of the old outdated greenhouses at Tunstall, Cauldon Park and Keele, there would be a massive reduction in fuel costs, and a saving to ratepayers. Right from the beginning just 6 men dealt with all the work involved in the G.2000 complex of eleven vast greenhouses, using a machine that could plant 18 to 20 thousand plants a day! It was quite a change from when bossman, Mr Harold Hancock, began work as apprentice gardener at Tunstall Park, when his first job was putting geraniums into clay pots by hand. However, when a group of us visited G.2000 in 1994, he told us that potting on by hand still proved more efficient as the machine had several drawbacks!

We were taken first into the massive seedling house, or propagator, where the trays were on beds of man-made tiny balls of lytag (made from 'fly ash' from a power station), under which heating pipes ran. There is a fogging system which when switched on caused the finest misting in just 5 minutes. It uses 2 gallons of water from the mains, not recycled (to prevent Legionnaires bacteria). Vermiculite is used for the seedlings and they need osmocote (granules of nitrate, phosphate and potassium, essential plant foods). Harold recommended spagnum moss peat for household gardeners and silicone sand to mix with it - never builders' sand!

We moved on to the other huge greenhouses where the temperatures were higher for exotic plants, grown for floral displays at civic events like the Lord Mayor's ball. There was a wide variety of plants, including poinsettias. Someone asked why these were so hard to keep after Christmas and Harold explained that after they had been brought to perfection by the specialist growers, they would be wrapped and shipped to wholesalers and then on to small distributers, being kept in cold conditions, and so on to shopkeepers who would again keep them in the cold along with cut flowers for sale. Once bought, at the coldest time of the year, they would be carried home, in the cold, and placed on cold windowsills..... all this cold being completely unsuitable for such plants! No wonder they wilted! Though often they valiantly kept their good looks for a fortnight or so before succumbing.

As we went through the other greenhouses Harold told us how, when they first began to work there, they came across drawbacks to the smooth running of the system; for example, overhead sprayers caused water to collect on pipes and brackets, which dripped off onto the plants below, causing them to become waterlogged. It must have been challenging.

The selection of plants is carefully made each year, the most showy blooms and foliage being used, Harold attending open days held by major suppliers like Colgreaves. He recommended tripoid marigolds 'Summer Sulphur'; geraniums of course were always winners too.

When we asked Harold if they liked having visitors, he replied, *'Yes, most certainly!'* He said they sometimes felt like a *'leper colony'* as so few visitors ever went there. Perhaps being at the remotest end of Festival Park has something to do with that, and also that there is never any advertisement for Greenhouse 2000, and no sign of welcome on the outside!

We were happy to learn that they run at a profit. The previous three city greenhouses cost £60,000 a year to heat, whereas the bill for G. 2000 is a mere £17,000! Perhaps we could call Greenhouse 2000 the most efficient factory on Festival Park today!

TEN

PRAISE FROM AFAR

Now for a final word of praise for our Garden Festival, from a couple of Festival fanatics who live in a certain Pudding Lane, Canterbury. A few years back in a hospitable Lakeland farmhouse, where the cuisine and the friendship were outstanding, our new friends told us they had been to all the garden festivals in Britain, so naturally we asked them which they had enjoyed best. Their instant reply was Stoke's!

They had been to European festivals as well, and they were finding that their memories were tending to merge into one - a good excuse for me writing this description of our own! They said that nothing in England could compare with the Dutch 'floriodes', especially of Amsterdam and The Hague, not surprisingly since the Dutch have ten years in which to prepare for each one of theirs!

Their reasons for preferring Stoke's Festival were, firstly, that the main emphasis was on horticulture, on plants and gardening, and this led to an atmosphere of quality which was pleasing (Gateshead had an atmosphere of 'funfare'); secondly the richness of Etruria's history had impressed them, thirdly they felt that Stoke's Festival had benefited from its sheltered position in the valley of Etruria, where there was a greater chance for the gardens and woodlands to flourish. (They did not know of the difficulties caused by the four very hot months of 1984 and the havoc of the inclement weather of 1985 and 1986!) Our friends told us of much evidence of wind-burn elsewhere, especially at Liverpool and Gateshead.

All in all we can feel proud that the Etruria Garden Festival achieved so much on this overworked and historic parcel of ground.

Celebrations on the last day of the Festival.

Gardeners' lunch break.

Young musicians entertained on the Woodland bridge.

ELEVEN
FESTIVAL PARK

At the end of the Garden Festival Mr. Roy Southern, former City Council Leader and Chairman of the National Garden Festival Board, praised the dedication of the whole management team numbering 1,000 people at the peak time. Workers and consultants had worked far beyond normally expected standards, and ensured the great success of the festival.

The city in general benefited. Approach roads were improved, 18,000 trees planted with the help of local industries and school children, and buildings and private land nearby spruced up. The show houses by the boat-filled marina were snapped up quickly at the end of the festival. No other residential development took place. However new homes and other major improvements for the nearby area of Cobridge were soon to come to fruition. The canal-side 'China Garden' pub was upgraded and continues to provide a popular venue.

A fly-over by-pass, costing $3^{1}/_{2}$ million pounds, commissioned and paid for by St Modwens, was built at the main entrance to Festival Park, linking the very busy Etruria and Cobridge Roads. It is 170 metres long and two lane, and takes traffic over the Etruria roundabout. An extra bonus is that when you are travelling over it you have a splendid bird's-eye-view of developments on site: conversely going under it, if travelling to Hanley for example, you have an equally enjoyable view of the elegant bridge itself, within its setting of lovely flowerbeds.

The Woodland Ridge area was not offically opened to the public until 1992, but people were able to walk up there from the end of the festival, as many did including ourselves, with their dogs and children. In the spring of 1994 we saw that much pruning had been taking place, and we were able to collect 20 different species of twigs nearly all from these prunings, as well as 20 different types of seed pods or boxes. The wide variety of shrubs and wild flowers is a delight - just 10 minutes from our home in the heart of an industrial city!

Lively music for the visitors on the Southern Steps.

Final days of the Garden Festival. St Augustine's home for the aged is seen on the horizon.

Left, stone walling for the Festival, and right, the
Boys' Brigade presence at the Festival.

Below:
1996 - the 10th anniversary party of the Garden
Festival - with Eric Newton providing the music.

TWELVE
BEFORE AND AFTER

In February, 1988, St. Modwen PLC secured a 150 year lease of the total site of about 160 acres, 65 of which were to be for landscaped open space and 95 for development. The main elements for Festival Park were to be:

1) A major leisure complex agreed with the Rank Organisation, consisting of an entertainment section with 10 screen cinema and 30 lane ten pin bowling alley; an indoor sub-tropical fun pool with wave machines, flumes and rapides; and an outdoor dry ski centre with training and main slopes. This complex was completed in 1989 at a cost of 17 million pounds.

2) A retail park, occupying the previous large parking area and Festival Market space. Giant stores came into being which were immediately popular with the public. A food superstore was built near to where the old Racecourse Pits had been, at a cost of over 25 million pounds, completed in 1989.

3) A 4 star hotel complex, developed in association with Queen's Moat, and including the elegant Etruria Hall, was completed in 1991, at a cost of over 19 million pounds.

4) Superior office buildings were built for small and large enterprises, some specifically designed as headquarters for firms, and all with beautiful surrounding gardens. Tenants include banks, Hanley Economic Building Society, KPMG Peat Marwick, North Staffs Chamber of Commerce and the Secretary of State for the Environment, to name a few.

5) Light industrial warehousing premises

6) A large landscaped area with 3 lakes providing a lovely setting for other office blocks, including the St. Modwen Office; and the Woodland Ridge which continues to develop as an area of outstanding beauty and walkways.

The total development cost of around £100 million has proved to be the best example of inner city regeneration in the British Isles. I often think of Ernest Warrilow's prediction in his *History of Etruria* (1952) that in a few years time people would not believe what changes would take place in this village; and as we pass Festival Park on the main road up to Cobridge I try to imagine the utter amazement of people, if they ever paid a 'flying visit', who, like my dad, worked there in times gone by, Talking of wings, to mark the completion of the business and leisure park, St Modwens commissioned a 25 foot stainless steel sculpture of a swan in flight to stand at the entrance to the busy complex. Labelled a 'tin duck' by some councillors, it is the Company's logo.

The beauty of the area in the 1930s!

The Loopline joins the main line on the way to Stoke Station. (Alf Wakefield)

Early stages of regeneration.

Looking over the newly planted park to the Shelton Steelworks and Wolstanton Colliery beyond.

Building the Moat House Hotel.

A recent picture of the Moat House and the Marina.

The Marina today.

The Etruria Industrial Museum.

THIRTEEN
CITICISMS OF THE GARDEN FESTIVAL AND FESTIVAL PARK

As always when vast amounts of public money are being spent, there were criticisms of the festival and later developments, both from local people and visitors. One of these concerned the enormous traffic problems generated by the large shopping area at the site. In 1992 it was said that 700 cars passed by the entrance roundabout every hour, making it hazardous for pedestrians. So a fly-over metal (supplied by Shelton Steel Works) bridge was installed overnight, and came into use the next day: and a different arrangement for traffic flow and parking was put into action.This certainly helped, but I, personally, would not venture there at very busy times!

People were attracted to the large shops on site especially in view of easy, free parking, proving to be bad news for city centre shops, especially the smaller ones and causing the demise of many - this of course was a national trend which has continued ever since.

In 1993 it was reported that there was trouble at Festival Park, where young drivers were using the parking spaces for late night speed runs, and there were dark areas where drug pushers were congregating. A higher police presence in the form of horse boxes being stationed there, before the mounted police went on duty in the town centre of Hanley, addressed the problem at the time.

Some people were high in praise of Waterworld, the ski slope and the other amenities of the leisure complex, but complained that all were vastly expensive. A marvellous family day out could be had at Festival Park, one parent said, but 'it cost an arm and a leg'!

A criticism, which I completely agreed with, came from our former newsagent, who displayed dogs. He felt that the City Council had been very shortsighted in not retaining the arena, or some other large part of the site, for use as a display, athletic training, outdoor activities, and public events area for the people of Stoke-on-Trent. He spoke of public sportsfields and wonderful large open areas of other cities he had visited when attending dog shows.

Publicity was given a few years back to the sadly neglected parts of the old Garden Festival site, accompanied by some pretty miserable photos, and rude remarks about Stoke's backsliding. How some journalists enjoy their negativity! The truth was that it was impossible for the small gardens to be kept up, because there was no inexhaustable money tree. I was disappointed that Bridgemere Nurseries did not retain their lovely garden for Stoke, in view of the fact that the city's population provide some of the staunchest of their customers, year in year out! They uprooted the Stoke garden to use for the next festival site at Ebbw Vale in South Wales.

In the late 1990s I enjoyed seeing a collection of 250 great Garden Festival slides taken by a local enthusiast. But the main impression gained from the people who attended this show was that the prices of everything had been too high for many of our citizens. The season ticket proved a boon of course, but I was reminded that I did not have a go on the scenic railway, not did I eat or drink on site, because it was all too expensive - we had three growing sons at the time!

FOURTEEN
SECURITY AND SUPERVISION ON FESTIVAL PARK

Mr Frank Foy was Supervisor for services and security on the retail section of Festival Park until about 1995. There is a central office with good views of the whole area, which is held by Prudential Portfolio Managers Ltd, Property Division, who are based in London. They lease all the land on which the large retail premises were built, except for Morrisons. A high quality of maintenance and service is expected, including security, health, lighting, gardening and general upkeep.

Frank was a Stoke-on-Trent boy born and bred, and served in the army for 20 years, on high security work in Cyprus and Ireland. He applied for a job on the Garden Festival site in 1985. He was made organiser for services, responsible for teams of maintenance workers, cleaners and other staff, who served the public in their various capacities during the festival. He was 'delighted' to see local folk finding work... the sudden change in the face after long term unemployment was a joy to behold!

He continued all through the festival as security supervisor until December 1986 and thoroughly enjoyed his work. He was sad though to see the apathy of many ordinary citizens towards the festival, and noted that the majority of support came from the outskirts of the city and further afield. Maybe folk thought it too great an outpouring of civic cash, or was it the poor weather that put them off? Perhaps the reasons went deeper than that: there is a general apathy towards local government in this city - could it be due to 200 years of exploitation and hard labour, and little in the way of just remuneration for the ordinary working people?

Frank was enthusiastic about his work as 'caretaker' for Prudential's interests at Festival Park, which included seeking out contractors for the essential services, such as cleaning, gardening, lighting and general outside security. He was keen to employ local firms, but here again noted with some surprise the apathy of local firms in tendering for these jobs. He mentioned that at the time the onsite cleaning was done by just one man, namely Mr. Joe. Parker, an ex-Shelton Bar man, who was utterly reliable and thorough.

Litter became an immense problem, especially after MacDonalds opened their doors. The public in general seem to have little pride in keeping their surroundings free of litter, and since the City Council are in financial straits little seems to be being done to keep our towns neat and tidy, except for the main pedestrian areas. However I have noted with pleasure going past Festival Park that the work is ongoing to keep the verges clear, and the various colours of the shrubs as they burst into life again after the winter are a delight.

There were other problems to be dealt with of course, like stolen cars dumped on the site, and car thefts. Heartening news from the safety point of view came in 1997 with the announcement that a new crime busting CCTV system had been installed at Festival Park, at a cost of £135,000. Eight closed circuit cameras can zoom in on a face from 200 yards and produce a crystal clear image, even in the dark; and this has reduced car and shop crime, as well as dissuading gangs. The public in general can enjoy the atmosphere of a fairly relaxed visit to Festival Park at any time now, day or night. It is necessary, sadly, to add the word 'fairly', since we are in a society where it is always important to be vigilant.

FIFTEEN
THE MOAT HOUSE HOTEL AND ETRURIA HALL COMPLEX

The Moat House Hotel was the first major hotel to be built in the city for nearly a hundred years, and with the inclusion of Etruria Hall as a Conference Centre, it has become a venue for national and international gatherings. The 147 bedroomed hotel, built to blend with the Georgian architecture of the hall, has a lower ground floor overlooking ornate landscaped gardens, retained and embellished since the Garden Festival. On the opposite side, at the hotel's main entrance, the view is of the Festival Park main avenue. Two stylish suites with private executive lounges are named after celebrities connected with the city, Arnold Bennett, and Robert Powell, the actor. There is a 162 seater restaurant, and an air-conditioned ballroom for 500 guests. The upstairs Capabilities Bar (named after Josiah Wedgwood's friend and famous landscape designer, Capability Brown) is open all day; the downstairs Fountain Bar is much used by diners. It is very pleasant to go to the lobby in the afternoon for a cup of tea and home baked biscuits, at a moderate cost, in the sumptuous surroundings.

The Hall is accessed through a glazed walkway, and has 11 meeting rooms, three accommodating 90 people in theatre style, and one for 70 people receptions. There are 2 syndicate rooms, a boardroom which was originally Josiah's private study, and a training floor for delegates. In theory as many as 22 meetings can be going on at the same time!

Up on the roof there is a self watering garden, a larger than life chess board with giant foot-high pieces, and marvellous vistas of the Festival Park, the surrounding city areas and the Staffordshire countryside. Visitors come from all over the world; the Japanese in particular have a great interest in fine English china.

When the hotel was officially opened in 1991, a time capsule was buried in the grounds, containing a copy of the local Evening Sentinel and a sample of the hotel's unique tableware. The ceremony was performed by Lord Wedgwood and Sir Stanley Matthews, the Potteries legend. The Moat House tableware was produced by the two ceramic giants of the city, working together for the first time, Wedgwood and Royal Doulton. 'Festival' ware for the restaurant was designed by Royal Doulton, and 'Fountain' ware for the banqueting rooms by Wedgwood). Both sets were produced by each firm, half and half.

Many different events are staged at the Hotel. One event which caught my school teacher eye was a week long course for junior pupils from a local school on the aspects of running a hotel. Present practice (2001) is for a group of school children to spend six Fridays in a row at the hotel, learning how to cook a dinner and how to serve it. At the end of the period the parents of the children, along with the school head, are invited to a dinner at the Moat House which the children have helped to cook and then serve! One can imagine the delight and pride of parents and children alike. As the process carries on the best students are assessed and these help to prepare and serve a dinner which the Lord Mayor attends. Then the civic dignitary presents the students with awards for their achievement.

There is also a health and fitness centre and a luxurious swimming pool. Members of the public can join the club and enjoy these facilities.

SIXTEEN
1999 UPDATE ON GREENHOUSE 2000

Recently in the local paper there was a picture of the Lord Mayor and his wife visiting Greenhouse 2000 on its first official 'open day', which gave me the hope that it would become an annual event. We should celebrate our city's centre of horticultural excellence.

Greenhouse 2000 now produces 3 million plants a year! What is more - and hurrah for technology (I never thought to hear myself say that) - the heating bill has been reduced to under £10,000. This is amazing news especially considering the loveliness of the city floral displays, and is due largely to the efforts of Mr Peter MacMillan, City Energy Conservation Officer, who searches for the cheapest source of heat for many sections of city life. So says Bossman, Harold Hancock, still very much 'on top' of running Greenhouse 2000, now with just four assistants and one part timer. Water bills are also kept down as all the rain water is collected from the vast roofs.

I was privileged to be able to study a thesis about the development of Greenhouse 2000. Far from being boring and too scientific, proved to be very informative. Had it not been for the Garden Festival and Stoke's tremendous reclamation work, we should not have had our high-tech greenhouse at all, with its ideal site, close to good transport and marketing outlets.

Much study went into the design of Greenhouse 2000, especially in regard to the right type of glazing material. It had to be extremely durable to weather and, in this day and age, vandal damage, easy to clean and mend, excellent for light transmission and retention, stable and with large easy-to-handle panels requiring fewer structural bars, easy on the eye, and not laible to deteriorate in colour!

The layout has proved excellent, the central corridor has bays off to each side which serve the purpose of every type of culture, and each environment has automatic computer control with manual override if needed. During brief periods of very hot sun there are automatic screens to prevent scorching or dehydraton. There is artificial light for the plants to shorten the growth period, enabling all-year-round cropping and the forcing or delaying of flowering in plants and shrubs, all of which is good for market demands and more economical production. For those who know about such matters there is high density culture, multi-layer and shift culture, artificial sub-strata and tissue culture.

SEVENTEEN

UPDATE ON WATERWORLD

Waterworld was taken over from the Rank Organisation in 1999 by a group of business companies headed by Mr Mo Chaudry, local businessman and former cricketer for Hartshill and Newcastle C.C. He came to England 30 odd years ago as an 8 year old, when his parents emigrated from Pakistan. Mo, a sportsman from the start, trained at Madeley College in sports management, but found that his career took him into financial services and property, where he spent 17 years 'out of leisure' as he expressed it. He felt he was 'coming home' when he took over Waterworld, which he said was already the largest aquatic theme park in the Country - this surprised me when I thought of other large complexes, especially in seaside towns - and was attracting by far the largest number of visitors, since it stays open all through the year.

Mo's plans for the redevelopment and extension of Waterworld and the land nearby are exciting and far reaching, as they envisage a re-integration of former and new associates on this famous site; a 'Wedgwood New Connection' may yet become a reality.

A £250,000 refurbishment of the complex began immediately. Plans have been drawn up for a further increase in space and services, which include a bar for adults and an area for amusement machines and computers; and also a larger sports shop.

Outside the complex there are plans for the restoration of the water gardens, which run behind the Moat House Hotel and in front of Etruria Hall - the most exciting news since the Garden Festival itself, for the whole area had been let go recently.

Even more exciting are the plans for the use of the rest of the land at the other side of Waterworld, including the provision of a new health and fitness centre to be run by a private company, the establishment of a wildlife sanctuary, and most fascinating of all, the possibility of a waterways link with the Wedgwood Visitors' Centre at Barlaston, after redevelopment of the neglected canal ways! The idea of boat trips between Festival Park and Barlaston presents a great scenario for school children, and for parents and tourists galore! Wedgwood, Staffs Wildlife Trust and 'Groundwork' of Stoke-on-Trent are all involved

Mo bedazzled me with all these possibilities. But can business and dreams come together to bring these plans to fruition? He is very convincing....

A haven for birdlife with the new Steelworks in the background.

EIGHTEEN
HANLEY ECONOMIC BUILDING SOCIETY AND OTHER BUSINESSES

The HEBS was founded in 1854 by Earl Granville, owner of the huge Shelton Iron, Steel and Coal Works, and formerly known as Staffordshire Potteries Economic Permanent Building Society. What a marvellous businessman he must have been! The initial membership of local steelworkers has been extended to include people from all walks of life and the area covered, which remains predominantly local, has also expanded to cover the whole of the country.

After 138 years of sound business at their Hanley offices, they returned, in 1992, to their roots at Festival Park, to occupy the purpose-built Granville House, situated opposite to the Moat House Hotel.

From humble beginnings, when the first annual report referred to 'a year of great commercial depression and embarrassment', they recorded that $142^{3/4}$ shares had been subscribed and that assets stood at £629. In 1992 the Society's assets stood at more than £160 million! They are proud of their beginnings, their close links with the great steelworks, but they go forth into the future as very much a part of the new technological age. Sophisticated computers now provide all their offices in the UK with up-to-the-minute facilities. The level of HEBS mortgage arrears is one of the lowest in the business, due largely to their rigid lending policy, which will not allow people to borrow more than they can afford, and also to their lower than average rate of interest charged.

A report at the beginning of the new millenium said that the Hanley Economic last year achieved the best performance of its 145 year history, its total assets having just exceeded a quarter of a billion pounds! It has therefore made an unbreakable pledge to invest £10 million in regional community projects in the next decade! Chief executive, Brian Thomas, said the commitment to backing the 'home community' is because they know full well that their success is due to the local people of North Staffs and South Cheshire.

Environmental and educational issues will figure largely in the millenium pledge, with young people involved in theatre, music and literacy schemes benefitting. Many youngsters are already deeply and happily involved with ongoing work at the New Vic Theatre in-the-Round for example, which is great for performers and viewers alike! The Hanley is already a significant supporter of the City Council's Greensteps campaign, and better living conditions for the elderly and the Staffordshire Wildlife Trust are further areas of their concern.

IONIX

An example of 'high-tech' industry on the Festival Park is Ionix High Performance Wiring Systems. They manufacture advanced electronic systems for aeropsace, defence and other advanced engineering markets worldwide, attempting to keep a balance between military, civil and commercial.

THE SKI SLOPE

Another, separate development nearby has been the taking over of the dry ski slope, after more than a year out of action, by a Cheshire businessman and partner. Their plan to spend £100,000 to turn this into a centre of excellence is good news, and ongoing, if the happy comments heard on Radio Stoke recently from people using the facility are anything to go by.

The earliest headquarters of the Hanley Economic Building Society in Cheapside, and below the new headquarters on Festival Park opposite the Moat House Hotel.

The original plan of the Festival Park, now in 2002 much enlarged with an extension towards Cobridge called Festival Heights.

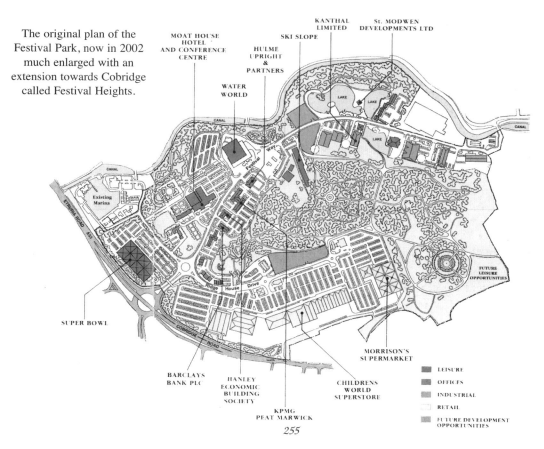

FINAL WORD

Recently we took our two small grandsons to see the many boats in the Marina at Festival Park, and we were delighted to watch the drawbridge being lifted to allow a holiday barge to enter from the canal, with good humour from one and all. A male swan did not seem in the least perturbed that he nearly got squashed by the boat - he was obviously quite used to the procedure. Moreover we had gone to see whether his 'missus' had hatched out the eggs yet, in the nest situated as large as life in the middle of the verge beside the Marina.

It struck me forcibly that no happier sight could be presented to show the great achievement of Festival Park! Here is a place in the heart of an industrial city where not only are a thousand needs catered for, but also where nature is appreciated and nurtured. Going, and staying, green is of vital importance for all of us, keeping in touch with Mother Nature is a must for our well being. It is a matter for pride and joy that the City is now deemed officially one of the greenest industrial centres of Great Britain.

BIBLIOGRAPHY

History of Etruria	Ernest Warrilow
1686 The History of Staffordshire	Dr. Plott
The Victoria County History of England, North Staffordshire	
Portrait of the Potteries	Bill Morland
A History of Staffordshire Iron Making	Roy Brassington
1898 Old Ordnance Survey Map	Godfrey Edition
The Potteries Loopline	Alan C. Baker
The Story of Wedgwood	Alison Kelly
Josiah Wedgwood	Robin Reilly
From Inferno to Flowers	Elaine Bryan and Neville Fisher
Selected letters of Josiah Wedgwood	edited by A. Finer and G.Savage
Tales of Old Staffordshire	Kathleen Laurence-Smith
Camden Britannia	ed. R.Gough, 1806
When I was a Child	Charles Shaw

Evening Sentinel, later The Sentinel, City News, Festival Brochures, The Way We Were